Guidelines for
MICROSOFT®
Office 2016
Workbook

Anita Verno • Jan Marrelli • Nancy Muir

PARADIGM
EDUCATION SOLUTIONS

St. Paul

Senior Vice President: Linda Hein
Editor in Chief: Christine Hurney
Senior Editor: Cheryl Drivdahl
Assistant Developmental Editors: Mamie Clark, Katie Werdick
Contributing Writer: Janet Blum
Testers: Pat Jarvis, Jeff Johnson, Barbara J. Shapiro
Director of Production: Timothy W. Larson
Production Editor: Elizabeth Mathews
Cover Designer: Jaana Bykonich
Text Designer and Senior Design and Production Specialist: Valerie King
Proofreader: Margaret Trejo
Indexer: Ina Gravitz
Vice President Information Technology: Chuck Bratton
Digital Projects Manager: Tom Modl
Vice President Sales and Marketing: Scott Burns
Director of Marketing: Lara Weber McLellan

Care has been taken to verify the accuracy of information presented in this book. However, the authors, editors, and publisher cannot accept responsibility for Web, e-mail, newsgroup, or chat room subject matter or content, or for consequences from application of the information in this book, and make no warranty, expressed or implied, with respect to its content.

Trademarks: Microsoft is a trademark or registered trademark of Microsoft Corporation in the United States and/or other countries. Some of the product names and company names included in this book have been used for identification purposes only and may be trademarks or registered trade names of their respective manufacturers and sellers. The authors, editors, and publisher disclaim any affiliation, association, or connection with, or sponsorship or endorsement by, such owners.

Photo Credits: Cover Dahabian/Shutterstock.com; **20** SoleilC/Shutterstock.com; **22** US Department of Agriculture; **81** Schoolhouse image from www.aware.org; screen caps of Microsoft products are used with permission from Microsoft.

We have made every effort to trace the ownership of all copyrighted material and to secure permission from copyright holders. In the event of any question arising as to the use of any material, we will be pleased to make the necessary corrections in future printings. Thanks are due to the aforementioned authors, publishers, and agents for permission to use the materials indicated.

ISBN 978-0-76387-128-4 (print)
ISBN 978-0-76386-749-2 (digital)

© 2017 by Paradigm Publishing, Inc.
875 Montreal Way
St. Paul, MN 55102
Email: educate@emcp.com
Website: www.ParadigmPublishing.com

Printed in the United States of America

25 24 23 22 21 20 19 18 17   5 6 7 8 9 10 11

Contents

Unit 1 Chapter 1 Computing Essentials

Study Resources

Study
Resources

*A chapter-based presentation with audio support
is available from this ebook page.*

Unit 1 Chapter 2 **Working with Student Data Files**

Study Resources

Study Resources

A chapter-based presentation with audio support, Margin Tips & Hints, and other study resources are available from this ebook page.

Unit 1 Chapter 3 **Managing Your Time with Outlook**

Study Resources

Study
Resources

A chapter-based presentation with audio support, Margin Tips & Hints, and other study resources are available from this ebook page.

Unit 2 **Office Suite**

Study Resources

Study
Resources

*A chapter-based presentation with audio support,
Margin Tips & Hints, and other study resources
are available from this ebook page.*

Word Chapter 1 **Creating Documents**

Study Resources

Study Resources

A chapter-based presentation with audio support, Margin Tips & Hints, and other study resources are available from this ebook page.

Features Review

Features Review

The Features Review available from this ebook page presents 10 multiple-choice questions to help you reinforce your understanding of the features covered in this chapter.

If you are a SNAP user, go to your Assignments page to complete the Features Review.

Skills Review

Review 1 **Check Spelling and Grammar and Proofread a Blog Post**

Skills   Enter and edit text, perform a spelling and grammar check, and set margins

Scenario   You host the blog *Healthy Techie* and have just drafted a post that discusses the importance of thumbs for today's smartphone users. Use the spelling and grammar checker to correct the paragraph and then proofread for errors that are not caught by the spelling and grammar check feature.

Steps

Student Data Files

1 Open the student data file named **C1R1-Thumbs** and save the file as **C1R1-Thumbs-Lastname**, but replace *Lastname* with your last name.

2 Type your name, a comma, and the current date on the first line of the document and then press Enter.

3 Use the spelling and grammar checker to correct errors in the text.

4 Proofread the document and correct any additional errors that you find. ***Hint:*** *The main paragraph should have seven complete sentences.*

5 Change the margins to 1 inch on the top and bottom and 2 inches on the left and right.

6 Save the file.

7 Print a hard copy or submit the file as directed by your instructor.

Student Name, Current Date

In today's technological society, your thumbs have a lot of work to do. Your thumbs need to be in shape so you can send messages quickly and accurately. They are critically important when working with your smartphone. Try to keep your thumbnails short. Long thumbnails tend to get in the way. And practice, practice, practice keying messages on your phone. The more you practice, the quicker and more accurate your typing will be and the sooner you can respond to your messages.

Completed
Review Preview

Review 2 Download and Modify a Template for an Insurance Premium Complaint Letter

Skills Enter and edit text, perform a spelling and grammar check, and create a document based on a template

Scenario You just received your annual bill for auto insurance and are surprised by the dramatic increase in premiums. You decide to send a letter of complaint to the president of your insurance company. You want to format your letter properly and include all the necessary information to ensure that it receives the attention it deserves.

Steps

1 Download the Letter of complaint about insurance premium increase template. You will need to search for the template using the phrase *complaint about insurance*. ***Hint:*** *In the New backstage area, type* complaint about insurance *in the search box and then press Enter.*

2 In the two [*Your Name*] placeholders, type your name. ***Hint:*** *Type your name in the first placeholder and then press Tab or click another part of the document; your name will automatically appear in the second placeholder.*

3 Type the street address, city, state, and zip code for your school in the appropriate placeholders.

4 In the [*Date*] placeholder, click the *Date* arrow and then click the *Today* option to automatically enter the current date.

5 In the two [*Recipient Name*] placeholders, type Janet Macintosh. ***Hint:*** *Type the words in the first placeholder, and they will automatically appear in the second placeholder.*

6   Janet is the president of ABC Insurance Company. Enter her title and the company name in the appropriate placeholders.

7   In the *[Street Address]* placeholder, type 123 Maple Street.

8   In the *[City, ST ZIP Code]* placeholder, type St. Paul, MN 55102.

9   In the *[Insurance Company Name]* placeholder, type ABC Insurance Company.

10 In the *[percent increase]* placeholder, type 50.

11 Use the spelling and grammar checker to locate and correct errors. Proofread the document to be sure it is correct.

12 Save the file with the name **C1R2-Insurance-Lastname**, but replace *Lastname* with your last name. You may see a message advising that your document will be upgraded to the newest file format. Click the OK button to upgrade the memo to the newest file format before saving.

13 Print a hard copy or submit the file as directed by your instructor.

Completed Review 2

Completed
Review Preview

Review 3 Change Document Properties and Insert Elements into a Breakfast Plan

Skills Enter and edit text; use the Show/Hide ¶ feature; use cut, copy, and paste; indent and add tabs using the ruler; insert a page break; and insert headers and footers

Scenario In an effort to get to class on time, you often run out the door without eating breakfast. Last week, you and a friend challenged each other to train for a half-marathon, and you now realize that you need a quick, healthy breakfast for energy to survive your busy morning at school—and your afternoon training session!

Steps

Student
Data Files

1 Open the student data file named **C1R3-Breakfast** and save it as **C1R3-Breakfast_ Lastname**, but replace *Lastname* with your last name.

2 Turn on Show/Hide ¶ to display formatting marks. ***Note:*** *Working with Show/Hide ¶ on will be helpful throughout this review exercise.*

3 Add to the document a header that includes your name at the left margin and the current date at the right margin. ***Hint:*** *Click the Insert tab, click the Header button in the Header & Footer group, and then click the* Blank (Three Columns) *option. Use the left and right placeholders, and delete the center placeholder.*

4 Add a footer that places a plain page number in the bottom center of the page.

5 On the first breakfast option line, which begins *2 fried eggs*, type Approximate calories before the number *500*. Be sure to include a space between the *s* at the end of calories and the *5* at the beginning of *500*.

6 Select the text you just typed, *Approximate calories*, copy it, and paste it before the number at the end of each of the next five breakfast options, from *Scrambled eggs with…* through *Fruit salad….* Again be sure you include a space between the *s* at the end of *calories* and the *5* at the beginning of *500*.

7 Select the list of breakfast options, beginning with *2 fried eggs* and ending with *Approximate calories 210*. Set left tabs at 2.25 inches and 4.75 inches. ***Hint:*** *You may need to make the ruler visible.*

8 Indent the first line of the paragraph that begins with *Breakfast is an* by 0.5 inch. ***Hint:*** *See the* Taking It Further *feature in Skill 6.*

9 Insert a page break at the start of the line that begins *A few breakfast*.

10 Use the spelling and grammar checker to correct any spelling and grammar errors in the text.

11 Turn off Show/Hide ¶ and then proofread the document to be sure it is correct.

12 Save the file.

13 Print a hard copy or submit the file as directed by your instructor.

Completed
Review Preview

SNAP Exercises

*If you are a SNAP user, go to your SNAP Assignments page
to complete additional exercises available for you.*

Word Chapter 2
Formatting Documents and Citing Sources

Study Resources

Study
Resources

A chapter-based presentation with audio support, Margin Tips & Hints, and other study resources are available from this ebook page.

Features Review

Features
Review

The Features Review available from this ebook page presents 10 multiple-choice questions to help you reinforce your understanding of the features covered in this chapter.

If you are a SNAP user, go to your Assignments page to complete the Features Review.

Skills Review

Review 1 Formatting an Essay about Exercise Equipment

Skills   Change font and font size, use formatting tools, apply styles, align text, format paragraph and line spacing, format text in columns, copy formatting with Format Painter, and insert a footnote

Scenario   You have written a brief essay about exercise equipment for your community's Healthy Living initiative. Use various formatting tools to highlight important information in the document.

Steps

Student
Data Files

1   Open the student data file named **C2R1-Equipment** and save the file as **C2R1-Equipment-Lastname**, but replace *Lastname* with your last name.

2   Insert a header that includes your name at the left margin and the current date at the right margin.

3   Insert a footer with a plain page number in the center.

4   Select the title *Exercise Equipment* and change the style to Heading 1. Set the font size to 22 points.

5   Justify the entire document. ***Hint:*** *Select all the text in the document and then change the alignment.*

6   Format the list of various types of exercise equipment (from *Treadmill* to *Balance board*) in three columns of equal width. ***Hint:*** *Turn on Show/Hide ¶ to be sure you select all the equipment names and their paragraph symbols.*

7   Set the line spacing for the body of the document—beginning with *Exercise equipment includes* and ending with *exercise program!*—to 1.15. ***Hint:*** *Select the specified text and then change the line spacing.*

8 Highlight the two paragraphs at the start of the document body—beginning with *Exercise equipment includes* and ending with *as the following:*—and set the spacing after paragraphs to 12 points.

9 In the body of the document—beginning with *Exercise equipment includes* and ending with *such as the following:*—italicize all four instances of the word *equipment*. **Hint:** *Italicize the first instance. Double-click the Format Painter button and then double-click the second instance; the second instance automatically adopts the same formatting as the first. Continue in this manner until you have italicized all instances of* equipment. *Click the Format Painter button again to turn off the feature.*

10 Underline the two instances of the word *gym*.

11 Insert a blank line above the final sentence of the document, which begins *Remember to check*.

12 Select the final sentence of the document, and then change the font size to 14 points and apply bold formatting.

13 Insert a footnote after the word *resistance* in the second sentence of the first paragraph (the sentence that begins *Exercise equipment may*). Type the body of the footnote as Resistance equipment uses weights and pulleys to permit individual adjustment.

14 Insert a footnote after the period that ends the second sentence of the first paragraph (the sentence that begins *Exercise equipment may*). Type the body of the footnote as Modern exercise equipment typically provides the ability to select the type of workout desired.

15 Save the file.

16 Print a hard copy or submit the file as directed by your instructor.

Completed Review 1

Completed
Review Preview

Review 2 **Formatting a List of Exercises and Estimated Average Calories Burned**

Skills   Change font and font size, use formatting tools, align text, create bulleted and numbered lists, and copy formatting with Format Painter

Scenario   You have drafted a paragraph listing a variety of exercise options and the estimated calories burned for the average individual. Your community's Healthy Living initiative would like to post this list to help people understand how calories burned are related to exercise. To make it easier for readers to see this connection, you decide to separate the activities and format them in a bulleted list.

Steps

Student
Data Files

1 Open the student data file named **C2R2-Calories** and save the file as **C2R2-Calories-Lastname**, but replace *Lastname* with your last name.

2 Insert a header that includes your name at the left margin and the current date at the right margin.

3 Insert a footer with a plain page number in the center.

4 Turn on Show/Hide ¶ to display formatting marks, and then separate the statements in the main body of the document (the paragraph beginning *After 30 minutes* and ending *burns 150 calories*.) into individual list items. **Hint:** *Delete the space before each statement and then press Enter to place each statement on its own line.* **Another Way:** *Use Find and Replace: Select the paragraph, search for . , and replace it with the paragraph mark (found in the* Replace Special *drop-down list).*

5 Add bullets to the list of statements beginning with *After 30 minutes* and ending with *burns 150 calories*. Change the bullets to check marks. Change the font of the bulleted items to 16-point Calibri.

6 Change the font of the title *Burning Calories* to 28-point Lucida Sans and center the title.

7 Use Format Painter to apply the title formatting to the final sentence of the document, which begins *Find something you*. Italicize the last sentence.

8 Save the file.

9 Print a hard copy or submit the file as directed by your instructor.

Completed Review 2

Completed
Review Preview

Review 3 Formatting a Report on How Yoga Benefits Families

Skills   Change font and font size, use formatting tools, align text, format paragraph and line spacing, insert citations using professional styles, and create a works cited page

Scenario   Your instructor has provided the draft of a term paper about the benefits of yoga and given you the assignment of formatting the report for submission. Your instructor has provided the following formatting guidelines:

Font: 12-point Times New Roman
Spacing: double
Alignment: left
Paragraph First line indentation: 0.5 inch
Header: your last name, a space, and the page number in the upper right corner
References: MLA Seventh Edition parenthetical citations
Works cited page: required

Skills

Student Data Files

1   Open the student data file **C2R3-Yoga** and save the file as **C2R3-Yoga-Lastname**, but replace *Lastname* with your last name.

2   Change the font for the entire document to 12-point Times New Roman.

3   Remove all blank lines. Set line spacing to double for the document. **Hint:** *Click the Show/Hide ¶ button to turn on the display of formatting marks, delete each extra paragraph mark, and then click the Show/Hide ¶ button again if you wish to work with it off.*

4   Highlight the body of the document—from the paragraph beginning *One way families* through the paragraph ending *from these advantages.*—and set paragraph indents and alignment as directed in the formatting guidelines given in the Scenario above.

5   At the top of page 1, complete the following tasks:
   a. Replace *Instructor's Name* with the name of your instructor.
   b. Replace *Course Name* with the name of your course.
   c. Replace *Current Date* with today's date written in the day-month-year style (e.g., 5 March 2017).

6   Type your name in parentheses after the author's name, *Julia Sanders, replacing the words Student Name.* **Note:** *Julia Sanders is the author of this paper. By enclosing your name in parentheses in this exercise, you are indicating that you modified the paper. When you write your own paper using MLA Seventh Edition style, you will type your own name as author and will not enclose it in parentheses.*

7   Center the title *Improving Activity Levels in All Families through Yoga.*

8   Insert a one-field header that contains your last name, followed by a space and then the page number. **Hint:** *Insert a header with one field (called a Blank header), type your last name, type a space, and then use the Page Number button to insert a simple plain page number at the current location. Make sure there is a blank line as the second line of the header. Right align the header. The header font should be the same as in the rest of the document: 12-point Times New Roman.*

9   Set the reference style to *MLA Seventh Edition.*

10 Add the following sources:

Type of Source	Book Section
Author	Tanasi, A.; Videira, C.; Newcomb, J.; Diaz, A.
Book Title	Behavior management: Traditional and expanded approaches
Year	2013
Pages	124-139
City	Landham, MD

Type of Source	Book
Publisher	University Press of America, Inc.
Author	Gillen, L.; Gillen, J.
Title	Yoga Calm for Children: Educating Heart, Mind, and Body
Year	2008
City	Portland, OR
Publisher	Three Pebbles Press, LLC

11 The following sources have values for both default fields and optional bibliography fields. For each source, enter data using the default fields that appear. Then insert a check mark in the *Show All Bibliography Fields* check box and enter the values for the optional fields.

Type of Source	Journal Article
Author	Satvika, G.; Buckley-Reed, A.; Alexander, L.; Chintakrindi, R.; Venice, L.; Patten Koenig, K.
Title	The effectiveness of a manualized yoga intervention on classroom behaviors in elementary school children with disabilities: A pilot study
Journal Name	Journal of Occupational Therapy, Schools, & Early Intervention
Year	2013
Pages	158-164
Volume (use optional field)	6
DOI (use optional field)	10.1080/19411243.2013.810942

Type of Source	Journal Article
Author	Hagins, M.; Haden, S.; Daly, L.
Title	A randomized controlled trial on the effects of yoga on stress reactivity in 6th grade students
Journal Name	Evidence-Based Complementary and Alternative Medicine
Year	2013
Volume (use optional field)	2013
DOI (use optional field)	10.1155/2013/607134

Type of Source	Web site
Author	Tilak, V.
Name of Web Page	The Benefits of Yoga for Kids
Year Accessed	2013
URL (use optional field)	http://www.parents.com/fun/sports/exercise/the-benefits-of-yoga-for-kids/

12 Enter the citations in the indicated locations using the Insert Citation tool. Be sure to delete the citation markers. Each citation marker begins and ends with **.

13 Place the insertion point at the end of the document and then insert a page break. Hint: Click the Page Break button in the Pages group on the Insert tab.

14 Use the Bibliography tool to create a works cited page. *Hint:* Click Works Cited *in the Bibliography drop-down list on the References tab.*

15 If necessary, modify the format of the works cited page so it conforms to the requirements of *MLA Seventh Edition.* Center the heading *Works Cited* and double-space the entire works cited section, beginning with the title and ending with the last line of the last citation.

16 Save the file.

17 Print a hard copy or submit the file as directed by your instructor.

Lastname 1

Julia Sanders (Student Name)

Instructor's Name

Course Name

Current Date

Improving Activity Levels in All Families through Yoga

One way families can improve activity level is through yoga. Yoga is a mind-body approach that has been shown to have positive influences on children and adults (Savita, Buckley-Reed and Alexander). According to Tanasi, et al., yoga consists of physical movement, mental awareness, and spiritual connection. Hagins, Haden, and Daly define yoga as "an ancient tradition that uses techniques of posture (asana), breath control (pranayama), and meditation, as well as moral and ethical observances" (1). As you can see, there are many different ways to define yoga. There are also many advantages families can gain from yoga.

Yoga has been shown to be beneficial for both adults and children. Since yoga has many different aspects to it, there are many different health benefits. According to Tanasi, et al., the physical practice of yoga improves flexibility, strengthens muscles, and releases tension. It also helps lower blood pressure and decrease heart rate. Since there is also a mental aspect of yoga, it has been shown that yoga helps people attain inner peace (Tanasi, Vidiera and Newcomb).

Children reap specific benefits from yoga that are slightly different from what adults gain. According to Gillen and Gillen, children who have taken yoga classes have shown improvement in academic performance in school. Tanasi, et al., add that children who have taken yoga classes exhibit increased memory and mental processing speed. They also have a longer attention span. Gillen and Gillen also suggest that yoga helps children make healthier choices

Lastname 2

with regard to food options, and stress management. In my opinion, these are two very important traits for children's overall health and well-being.

According to Gillen and Gillen, one trait of yoga is stillness. Children often have difficulty being still; however, yoga helps children develop strategies to display stillness throughout their day. Once these strategies are perfected during a yoga session, the children can then use these techniques when their lives become chaotic. One moment of chaos that Gillen and Gillen use as an example is when children are packing up to go home at the end of a school day. Children who know how to be still can remain calm even when there are many children rushing around them. Furthermore, according to Tanasi, et al., yoga has been shown to lower levels of aggression in children, and to improve their ability to follow directions and cooperate in groups.

According to Tilak, children who take regular yoga classes have better self-esteem. The challenges of the poses in the physical practice of yoga help children see how strong their bodies are. When children see and can feel their strong bodies, they become more confident. For example, when doing a balance posture in a yoga class, children are encouraged to fall and get right back up to try again. Children are also encouraged to stay calm when they fall. When children finally master a balance pose they are having difficulty with, their self-esteem and confidence increase (Tilak).

In addition to the benefits mentioned above for all children, yoga has specific benefits for children with disabilities (Savita, Buckley-Reed and Alexander). According to Satvika, et al., yoga is often used in a behavior intervention plan for children with disabilities. Satvika et al., conducted a study in which 51 children with disabilities, ages 5 to 9, participated in 60 minutes of yoga every day first thing in the morning. The children in the study had disabilities such as autism spectrum disorder, multiple physical handicaps, and developmental disabilities. After 26

Lastname 3

weeks, the study found improved academic productivity, increased levels of independence and attention, and better self-regulation. Gillen and Gillen also found yoga to be beneficial for children with conditions such as attention deficit disorder (ADD) and attention deficit hyperactivity disorder (ADHD). As mentioned previously, Gillen and Gillen found that including moments of stillness in yoga practice encouraged children to use a moment of stillness when faced with chaos. Similarly, yoga teaches a child with ADD or ADHD to use moments of stillness to control their behavior. When these children use moments of stillness, they are able to focus and pay attention with more ease (Gillen and Gillen).

In my opinion, yoga is the perfect activity for families. As the research above states, the advantages of yoga for adults, children, and children with special needs are unique. It is my belief that all families who participate in yoga programs will benefit from these advantages.

Lastname 4

Works Cited

Gillen, L. and J. Gillen. *Yoga Calm for Children: Educating Heart, Mind, and Body.* Portland, OR: Three Pebbles Press, LLC, 2008.

Hagins, M., S. Haden and L. Daly. "A randomized controlled trial on the effects of yoga on stress reactivity in 6th grade students." *Evidence-Based Complementary and Alternative Medicine* 2013 (2013).

Savita, G., et al. "The effectiveness of a manualized yoga intervention on classroom behaviors in elementary school children with disabilities: A pilot study." *Journal of Occupational Therapy, Schools, & Early Intervention* 6 (2013): 158-164.

Tanasi, A, et al. "Behavior Management: Traditional and Expanded Apporaches." Landham, MD: University Press of America, Inc., 2013. 124-139.

Tilak, V. *The Benefits of Yoga for Kids.* n.d. 2013.

<http://www.parents.com/fun/sports/exercise/the-benefits-of-yoga-for-kids/>.

Completed
Review Preview

SNAP Exercises

If you are a SNAP user, go to your SNAP Assignments page to complete additional exercises available for you.

Word Chapter 3 **Working with Tables and Objects**

Study Resources

Study
Resources

*A chapter-based presentation with audio support,
Margin Tips & Hints, and other study resources
are available from this ebook page.*

Features Review

Features
Review

*The Features Review available from this ebook
page presents 10 multiple-choice questions to
help you reinforce your understanding of the
features covered in this chapter.*

 SNAP

*If you are a SNAP user, go to your Assignments
page to complete the Features Review.*

Skills Review

Review 1 **Use Table Formatting on a Visitors Log**

Skills Convert text to tables, change page orientation, insert and delete rows and columns in a table, and insert media

Scenario You are the office receptionist for *Guidelines for Healthy Living Magazine*. Use table formatting to improve the appearance of a log that helps the magazine staff keep track of upcoming visitor appointments.

Steps

Student
Data Files

1 Open the student data file **C3R1-Visitors** and save the file as **C3R1-Visitors-Lastname**, but replace *Lastname* with your last name.

2 Change the page orientation to landscape and set the margins to Narrow.

3 Change the font of the title *Today's Visitors Log* to 18-point Calibri. **Note:** *It is currently Calibri (Body).*

4 Convert the body of the document—the 16 lines of text below the title—to a table using the *AutoFit to contents* option with tabs separating the text. **Hint:** *Turn on Show/Hide ¶, select all 16 lines including the paragraph symbol at the end of each line, select* AutoFit to contents *in the Convert Text to Table dialog box, and ensure that* Tabs *is selected In the* Separate text at *section of the dialog box. Leave Show/Hide ¶ turned on for the remaining steps in this review.*

5 Adjust the right border of each column to the following specified inch mark on the ruler, ensure each column uses only one line per visitor. **Hint:** *Adjust the columns from right to left (starting with the column* To See *and ending with the column* Visitor's Name.

To See	9
AM/PM	8
Time	7
Email Address	6.0
Cell Phone	3.5
Visitor's Name	2

6. Apply bold formatting to all column headings.

7. Insert a row after the row that begins *Zachary Taylor* and type the following data in the appropriate columns: Millard Fillmore, 703.778.4455, mfillmore@ParadigmCollege.net, 2:00, PM, Jon. Proofread your entry. ***Hint:*** *To force the email address to appear as a hyperlink, press the Tab key after typing the email address.*

8. James Monroe has accidentally been entered twice in the same time slot. Delete the second row that begins *James Monroe*.

9. Peter Smith has cancelled his appointment. Delete the row that begins *Peter Smith*.

10. On the first line of the document, insert the student data file **C3R1-Logo**, which is the *Guidelines for Healthy Living Magazine* logo. Press Enter two times to insert one blank line after the logo. Center the logo. ***Hint:*** *Use Show/Hide ¶ to be sure you insert the logo on the first line and insert exactly one blank line following the logo. After inserting the logo, click the picture and then click the* Center *button.*

11. Insert a header with your name on the left and the current date on the right.

12. Save the file.

13. Print a hard copy or submit the file as specified by your instructor.

Completed Review 1

S   Current Date

Guidelines
FOR HEALTHY Living Magazine

Today's Visitors Log

Visitor's Name	Cell Phone	Email Address	Time	AM/PM	To See
John Adams	202.145.3636	jadams@ParadigmCollege.net	8:00	AM	Steve
James Madison	202.558.6523	jmadison@ParadigmCollege.net	8:30	AM	Steve
James Monroe	703.985.6312	jmonroe@ParadigmCollege.net	9:00	AM	Steve
Martin Van Buren	202.775.6528	mvanburen@ParadigmCollege.net	9:45	AM	Steve
William Henry Harrison	202.554.1212	wharrison@ParadigmCollege.net	10:30	AM	Jon
John Tyler	703.887.5465	jtyler@ParadigmCollege.net	11:00	AM	Steve
Zachary Taylor	703.335.6452	ztaylor@ParadigmCollege.net	1:00	PM	Jon
Millard Fillmore	703.778.4455	mfillmore@ParadigmCollege.net	2:00	PM	Jon
Franklin Pierce	703.225.3451	fpierce@ParadigmCollege.net	3:30	PM	Amanda
James Buchanan	703.123.6589	jbuchanan@ParadigmCollege.net	4:00	PM	Jon
Rutherford B. Hayes	703.331.7452	rhayes@ParadigmCollege.net	5:15	PM	Amanda
James Garfield	703.852.9645	jgarfield@ParadigmCollege.net	6:45	PM	Amanda
Chester Arthur	703.345.6958	carthur@ParadigmCollege.net	8:00	PM	Amanda
Benjamin Harrison	202.642.8132	bharrison@ParadigmCollege.net	8:30	PM	Amanda

Completed
Review Preview

Review 2 Use a Table to Create an Exercise Class Schedule

Skills Create tables, merge rows or columns in a table, format tables, insert SmartArt, insert media, resize media, and align and format media

Scenario You are the office manager for a busy local gym. Saturday classes are popular, and nobody wants to miss a favorite class. Create a schedule to let members know the time and location of all the Saturday exercise classes.

Steps

Student
Data Files

1 Open the student data file **C3R2-Schedule** and save the file as **C3R2-Schedule-Lastname**, but replace *Lastname* with your last name.

2 Change the font size of the title *Exercise Class Schedule* to 24 points and the font color to Green, Accent 6.

3 Change the font size of the subtitle *Exercise Classes for Saturday* to 16 points and the color to Green, Accent 6.

4 Move the insertion point to the third blank line after the subtitle *Exercise Classes for Saturday* and then insert a table containing 5 columns and 15 rows. **Hint:** *Turn on Show/ Hide ¶ to be sure you have exactly two blank lines (two paragraph symbols) before the table.*

5 Type the values for the table cells as shown below. **Note:** *The italicized black numbers to the left of the table are for reference in Steps 6–11; do not type those numbers.*

	AM/PM	Time	Gym	Studio	Spin Room
1	AM/PM	Time	Gym	Studio	Spin Room
2	The gym opens at 8:00 AM on Saturday mornings.				
3	AM	8:00			
4		9:00			Beginning Spin
5		10:00			
6		11:00		Cardio Workout	
7	PM	12:00	Muscle Maker		Spin
8		1:00		Hip-hop	
9		2:00	Trampoline Exercises	Step	
10		3:00			Advanced Spin
11		4:00	Fat Burn Workout	Shake It Off	
12	Evening	5:00			
13		6:00	Kickboxing	Yoga	
14		7:00		Pilates	Spin
15	The gym closes at 8:00 PM on Saturday evenings.				

6 Apply bold formatting to row 1 in the table.

7 Merge all columns in row 2 so there is only one column in that row.

8 Merge all columns in row 15 so there is only one column in that row.

9 Merge the cells in rows 3–6 of the *AM/PM* column so there is only one row containing the word *AM* for those cells.

10 Merge the cells in rows 7–11 of the *AM/PM* column so there is only one row containing the word *PM* for those cells.

11 Merge the cells in rows 12–14 of the *AM/PM* column so there is only one row containing the word *Evening* for those cells.

12 Remove the outside border from the table.

13 Use the Online Pictures button in the Illustrations group on the Insert tab and type exercise in the search box to find an image similar to the one shown in Completed Review 2. Insert the image as shown in the completed skill and then apply the following effects:
   a. Change text wrapping to square.
   b. Set the image height to 1.5 inches.
   c. Move the image to align with the top of the title *Exercise Class Schedule* and with the right margin of the document.

14 Insert a header that includes your name at the left margin and the current date at the right margin.

15 At the end of the document, add a blank line so that two paragraph symbols appear after the table.

16 In the new blank line, insert the Equation SmartArt graphic. **Hint:** *Click the* Process *command in the left panel of the* Choose a SmartArt Graphic *dialog box and then scroll down in the middle panel to find the* Equation *option.*

17 Type the following text for the three bullet points in the graphic: Eat Right, Exercise, Feel Great!.

18 Change the colors of the graphic to Colorful Range - Accent Colors 4 to 5.

19 Save the file.

20 Print a hard copy or submit the completed file as directed by your instructor.

Completed Review 2

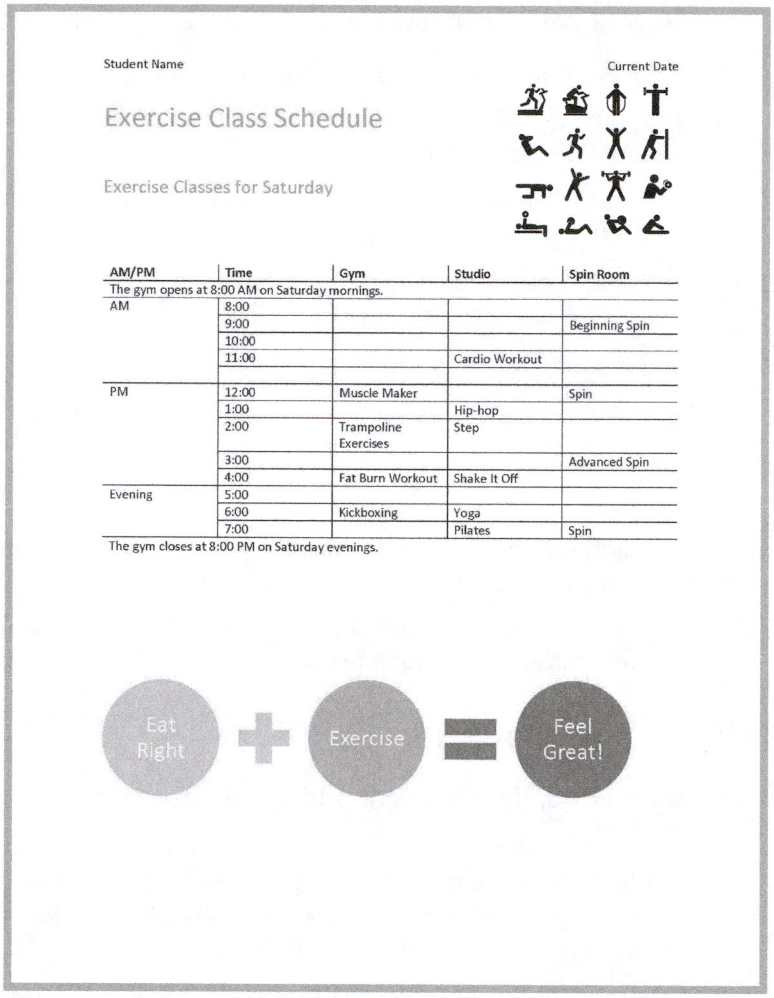
Student Name

Current Date

Exercise Class Schedule

Exercise Classes for Saturday

AM/PM	Time	Gym	Studio	Spin Room
The gym opens at 8:00 AM on Saturday mornings.				
AM	8:00			
	9:00			Beginning Spin
	10:00			
	11:00		Cardio Workout	
PM	12:00	Muscle Maker		Spin
	1:00		Hip-hop	
	2:00	Trampoline Exercises	Step	
	3:00			Advanced Spin
	4:00	Fat Burn Workout	Shake It Off	
Evening	5:00			
	6:00	Kickboxing	Yoga	
	7:00		Pilates	Spin
The gym closes at 8:00 PM on Saturday evenings.				

Completed Review Preview

Review 3 Create an Attractive Newsletter

Skills Change page orientation, insert SmartArt, insert visual media, resize media, and align and format media

Scenario You have been asked to format the text for the annual *Guidelines for Healthy Living Magazine* newsletter in an attractive three-column layout.

Steps

Student Data Files

1 Open the student data file **C3R3-Food** and save the file as **C3R3-Food-Lastname**, but replace *Lastname* with your last name.

2 Change the orientation to landscape.

3 Set the margins to Narrow.

4 Insert a one-field header (called a Blank header) and then modify it as follows:
   a. Delete the placeholder.
   b. Insert the student data file **C3R3-Logo**, which is the *Guidelines for Healthy Living Magazine* logo. Set text wrapping to Square.
   c. In the first line of the header, type Annual Newsletter and then right align the text. ***Hint:*** *Start by turning on Show/Hide ¶ and then place the insertion point before the first paragraph symbol in the header. You may want to leave Show/Hide ¶ turned on for the remaining steps in this review.*

d. Change the font effect of the text *Annual Newsletter* to small caps. **Hint:** *Select the text, click the dialog box launcher in the Font group on the Home tab to open the Font dialog box, click the* Small caps *check box to insert a check mark, and then click the OK button.*

e. Change the font size of the text *Annual Newsletter* to 18 points and the font color to Light Blue.

f. Delete any blank lines below the text *Annual Newsletter*.

5 Select the last line of text in the document (beginning *Adapted from the*), remove it and place it on the Clipboard, insert a footer in the document, and then paste the text from the Clipboard into the footer. **Hint:** *Select the last line of text, click the Cut button in the Clipboard group on the Home tab, insert a blank footer, and then click the Paste button.*

6 Center the footer text and apply italic formatting. Delete any blank lines below the footer text.

7 In the first line of the document, replace *Student Name* with your name and *Current Date* with today's date, right align the text, and then insert three blank lines.

8 Select the body of the newsletter—from the line that begins *10 Tips for* through the line that ends *and t'ai chi.*—and complete these tasks:
a. Change the line spacing to single and the spacing after paragraphs to 6 points.
b. Create three columns of equal width.

9 Change the four boldfaced headings (*10 Tips for…*, *How Activity and…*, *The Importance of…*, and *A Few Types…*) to small caps and set the font color to Green, Accent 6. **Hint:** *Format the first heading and then use the Format Painter to copy the formatting to the remaining headings.*

10 Select the 10 tips—from the line that begins *Balance calories* through the line that begins *Drink water*—and apply the numbered list formatting. Use the Decrease Indent button in the Paragraph group on the Home tab to force the numbers to the left margin.

11 Insert a column page break to force the heading *A Few Types of Physical Activity* to appear at the top of the third column. **Hint:** *Place the insertion point in front of the heading, click the Layout tab, click the Breaks button in the Page Setup group, and then click the* Column *option in the drop-down list.*

12 Delete the blank line above the heading *The Importance of Physical Activity*.

13 Set the spacing before paragraphs to 12 points for the heading *The Importance of Physical Activity*.

14 Insert the student data file **C3R3-MyPlate**, which is the ChooseMyPlate.gov placemat image, in the section with the heading *How Activity and Nutrition Work Together*. **Hint:** *Place the insertion point at the end of the heading line and then insert the image.* Set text wrapping to Tight and adjust the width of the image to 1.5 inches. Place the image just below the heading, with the right margin of the image aligned with the right margin of the heading.

15 Use the Shapes tool to draw a 10-inch line between the logo and the body of the newsletter, extending from the left margin to the right margin. Change the color to Black.

16 Use the Shapes tool to draw a rectangle enclosing the heading *How Activity and Nutrition Work Together* and the paragraph that follows it (beginning with *Physical activity* and ending with *eating less.*). Change the shape outline to Light Blue and the shape fill to No Fill.

17 Save the file.

18 Print a hard copy or submit the file as directed by your instructor.

Guidelines FOR HEALTHY Living
Magazine

10 TIPS FOR MAKING HEALTHY FOOD CHOICES

1. Balance calories. Find out how many calories you need for a day as a first step in managing your weight. Being physically active also helps you balance calories.
2. Enjoy your food, but eat less. Eating too fast or when your attention is elsewhere may lead to eating too many calories. Pay attention to hunger and fullness cues before, during, and after meals.
3. Avoid oversized portions. Use a smaller plate, bowl, and glass. When eating out, choose a smaller size option, share a dish, or take home part of your meal.
4. Eat healthy foods more often. Eat more vegetables, fruits, whole grains, and fat-free or low-fat (1%) milk and dairy products.
5. Make half your plate fruits and vegetables.
6. Switch to fat-free or low-fat (1%) milk.
7. Make half your grains whole grains. Substitute a whole-grain product for a refined product—such as whole wheat bread instead of white bread or brown rice instead of white rice.
8. Eat less healthy foods less often. Cut back on foods high in solid fats, added sugars, and salt. Use these foods as occasional treats, not everyday foods.
9. Compare sodium in foods. Use the Nutrition Facts label to choose lower-sodium versions of foods.
10. Drink water instead of sugary drinks.

HOW ACTIVITY AND NUTRITION WORK TOGETHER

Physical activity and nutrition work together for better health. Being active increases the amount of calories burned.

As people age, their metabolism slows, so maintaining energy balance requires moving more and eating less.

THE IMPORTANCE OF PHYSICAL ACTIVITY

Regular physical activity can produce long-term health benefits. People of all ages, shapes, sizes, and abilities can benefit from being physically active. The more physically active you are, the greater the health benefits.

A FEW TYPES OF PHYSICAL ACTIVITY

Aerobic activities make you breathe harder and make your heart beat faster. Aerobic activities can be moderate or vigorous in their intensity. Vigorous activities take more effort than moderate ones. For moderate activities, you can talk while you do them, but you can't sing. For vigorous activities, you can only say a few words without stopping to catch your breath.

Muscle-strengthening activities make your muscles stronger. These include push-ups and weight lifting. It is important to work all the different parts of the body—legs, hips, back, chest, stomach, shoulders, and arms.

Bone-strengthening activities make your bones stronger. These activities produce a force on the bones that promotes growth and strength.

Balance and stretching activities enhance physical stability and flexibility, which reduces risk of injuries. Examples are gentle stretching, dancing, yoga, martial arts, and t'ai chi.

Adapted from the USDA Center for Nutrition Policy and Promotion's ChooseMyPlate.gov website.

Completed
Review Preview

SNAP Exercises

SNAP

If you are a SNAP user, go to your SNAP Assignments page to complete additional exercises available for you.

Word Chapter 4 Finalizing and Sharing Documents

Study Resources

Study Resources

A chapter-based presentation with audio support, Margin Tips & Hints, and other study resources are available from this ebook page.

Features Review

Features Review

The Features Review available from this ebook page presents 10 multiple-choice questions to help you reinforce your understanding of the features covered in this chapter.

If you are a SNAP user, go to your Assignments page to complete the Features Review.

Skills Review

Review 1 Have the Courage to Meet the Three Bears

Skills Turn on and view Track Changes, and make changes and add comments

Scenario The story of Goldilocks and the three bears has entertained children for more than a century. You volunteer for a nonprofit organization that creates audio recordings of children's stories, and you have been asked to help correct mistakes in the script for this recording. Use Track Changes in the Tracking group on the Review tab to correct the original document, and add a comment identifying the original source of the story.

Steps

Student Data Files

1 Open the student data file named **C4R1-Goldilocks** and save it as **C4R1-Goldilocks-Lastname**, but replace *Lastname* with your last name.

2 Turn on Track Changes and set *Display for Review* to *All Markup*.

3 Change the style for the first line, *Goldilocks and the Three Bears*, to Title.

4 In the title, select the words *Three Bears* and insert a comment, typing this as the comment text: Original fairy tale recorded by Robert Southey in 1837.

5 Insert a header with your name on the left and the current date on the right.

6 Insert a footer with a plain page number centered on the page.

7 With Track Changes turned on, make the following corrections:
   a. In the first paragraph, which begins *Once upon a*, change *Golden Locks* to Goldilocks.
   b. In the second paragraph, which begins *At the table*, change *pudding* to porridge.
   c. In the third paragraph, which begins *This porridge is too hot!* change *examined* to exclaimed.
   d. In the seventh paragraph, which begins *"Oh my*, change *Oh my* to Ahhh.
   e. In the 14th paragraph, which begins *Goldilocks was very*, insert the word first before the word *bed* in the second sentence, so it reads *She lay down in the first bed, but it was too hard.*

f. Also in the 14th paragraph, delete the second-to-last word, *fast*.

g. In the 22nd paragraph, which begins *They decided to*, change *Father* to Papa.

h. In the 25th paragraph, which begins *Just then, Goldilocks* change *Cute* to Help.

8   Save the document.

9   Print a hard copy or submit the file as directed by your instructor.

Completed Review 1

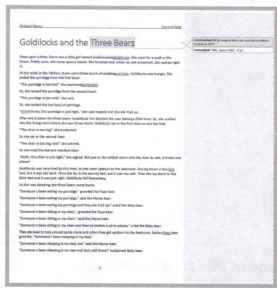
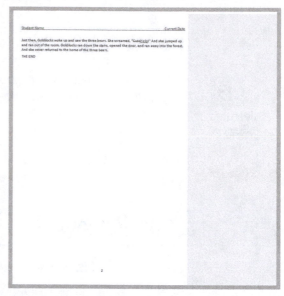

Completed
Review Preview

Review 2   Revise a Poorly Edited Nursery Rhyme

Skills   Turn on and view Track Changes and accept or reject changes and review comments

Scenario   "One, two…" is a nursery rhyme that is a favorite among children. They have fun reciting the words while learning about rhymes and counting. An editor has reviewed this version of "One, two…" and made changes to fix problems she found. Unfortunately, the editor's suggestions are not all correct. The original version is shown in Completed Review 2. Compare the words in the original version with the edited version. Accept or reject the editor's changes as necessary to make the edited version match the original version. After acting on the comments, delete them. Do not make any other changes to the text.

Steps

Student
Data Files

1   Open the student data file named **C4R2-NRhyme** and save it as **C4R2-NRhyme-Lastname**, but replace *Lastname* with your last name.

2   Turn off the Track Changes feature and set *Display for Review* to *All Markup*.

3   Insert a header with your name on the left and the current date on the right.

4   In the document body, accept or reject the changes as instructed below, so that the document matches the Completed Review 2.

a. Accept the format change for the title, *"One, two.…"*

b. Accept the format change for the author line, *by Mother Goose*.

c. Accept the blank line inserted under the author line. **Hint:** *Turn on Show/Hide ¶ to see the paragraph marker*.

d. Reject the change of *six* to *seven*.

e. Accept the change of *even* to *straight*.

f. Read and then delete the comment related to the word *delve*.

g. Reject the change of *Maids* to *Queens*.

5 Save the document.

6 Print a hard copy or submit the file as directed by your instructor.

Completed Review 2

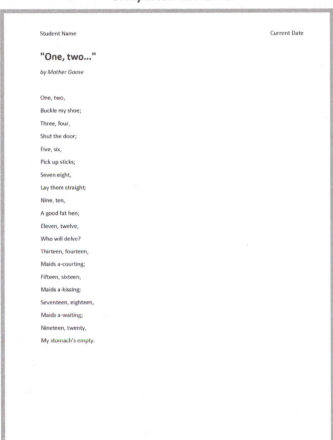

Completed
Review Preview

Review 3 **Finalize and Share a Memo**

Skills Send a document for editing via email, share a file for editing on OneDrive, and create a PDF file

Scenario You are the administrative assistant for the nonprofit organization Audio Access to Children's Literature. The office manager has asked you to finalize a memo about a planned phone system upgrade and then send it to the editorial director and production manager. Make the requested changes to the memo, create a PDF file, and then send the file as an email attachment or share it on OneDrive.

Steps

Student
Data Files

1 Open the student data file named **C4R3-Phone** and save it as **C4R3-Phone-Lastname**, but replace *Lastname* with your last name.

2 Replace the words *Student Name* with your name and the words *Current Date* with the current date in the format Month dd, yyyy (e.g., March 7, 2018).

3 Format the word *Memo* so it is right-aligned and 48-point Script MT Bold.

4 Save the document without closing it.

5 Resave the document as a PDF file. Use the same name as your Word document: **C4R3-Phone-Lastname.**

6 Share the PDF file with your instructor by sending it as an email attachment or by posting and sharing it on OneDrive. **Note:** *Your instructor may provide different instructions for submission.*

Completed Review 3

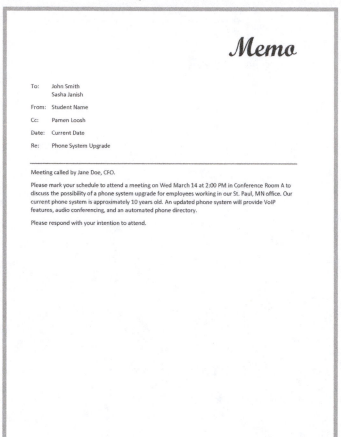

Completed
Review Preview

SNAP Exercises

 SNAP

If you are a SNAP user, go to your SNAP Assignments page to complete additional exercises available for you.

Unit 3 **Word**

Skills Assessment

Assessment 1 **"Ergonomically Correct" Handout**

Skills **CH1:** Enter and edit text; use the Show/Hide ¶ feature; use cut, copy, and paste; set margins; insert headers and footers **CH2:** Change font and font size; use formatting tools; apply styles; align text; create bulleted and numbered lists; format text in columns; copy formatting with Format Painter **CH3:** Insert media; resize media; align and format media **CH4:** Share a file for editing on OneDrive; Create a PDF file

Scenario You work part-time in the media center at your school, and you know that most students spend a lot of time at the computer. You have recently become aware that extended computer use can place a huge strain the body. You prepare a handout about creating an ergonomically appropriate environment to share with students who visit the media center. Add formatting to the handout to make it attractive and easy to read.

Steps

Student
Data Files

1 Open the student data file named **U3A1-Ergonomics** and save it as **U3A1-Ergonomics-Lastname**, but replace *Lastname* with your last name.

2 Insert a header with your name on the left and the current date on the right.

3 Apply the Heading 1 style to the title, *Reduce the Strain! Cut the Pain!* Change the font size to 26 points and apply bold formatting.

4 Apply the Heading 2 style to the subtitle, *Create an Ergonomically Appropriate Environment.* Apply italic formatting.

5 Apply the Subtle Reference style to the headings *What Is Ergonomics?* and *Ergonomic Tips for Computer Users.* Change the font size to 14 points and apply bold formatting.

6 Apply the Subtle Reference style to the four tip headings: *Working Area, Posture, Breaks,* and *Keyboarding.* Apply bold formatting to each tip heading. **Hint:** *Change the format for the first tip heading, and then use Format Painter to copy the formatting to the other three tip headings.*

7 Move the "Breaks" section—which begins with the line *Breaks* and ends with the blank line below the text line *Give your eyes…*—to be above the "Posture" section. **Hint:** *Turn on Show/Hide ¶. Cut the "Breaks" section, including the paragraph symbol below the last line of text; place the insertion point at the beginning of the* Posture heading; *and then paste the "Breaks" section. Leave Show/Hide ¶ turned on for the remaining steps in this assessment.* Check to be sure there is one blank line above each of the tips headings: *Breaks, Posture,* and *Keyboarding.* Add or delete blank lines as needed.

8 Apply the Narrow margin setting to the entire document.

9 Change the layout for the "Ergonomic Tips for Computer Users" section to two-column. **Hint:** *Highlight the text beginning with the heading* Working Area *and ending with the paragraph symbol at the end of the line* Do not use….

10 Place check-mark bullets in front of the tips in each of the four tip sections. Do not bullet the tip headings.

11 Delete the blank lines above the tip headings *Breaks, Posture,* and *Keyboarding.* These section separators are no longer needed. **Hint:** *Use Show/Hide ¶ to find the paragraph symbols for these blank lines.*

12 Delete the blank line above the last line of text, which begins *Work comfortably!*

13 Highlight the last line of text, apply the Heading 1 style, and center the text.

14 Place the insertion point at the end of the line that begins What Is Ergonomics? Use the Online Pictures tool, with the search phrase computer keyboard posture, to find and insert the graphic shown in Completed Assessment 1, or a similar image. If you cannot find the exact image shown, select another appropriate graphic.

15 Use the Picture Tools Format tab to change the text wrapping for the image to *square* and the width to 1.5 inches.

16 Position the image to the right of the *What Is Ergonomics?* section, aligning the top of the image with the top of the section heading and the right edge of the image with the right margin of the document, as shown in Completed Assessment 1.

17 Save the document.

18 Resave the document as a PDF file. Use the same name as your Word document: **U3A1-Ergonomics-Lastname**.

19 Share the PDF file with your instructor by sending it as an email attachment or by posting and sharing it on OneDrive. ***Note:*** *Your instructor may provide different instructions for submission.*

Completed Assessment 1

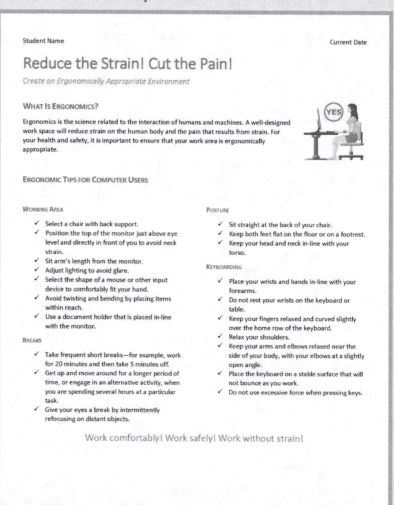

Completed
Assessment
Preview

Assessment 2 Fitness Equipment Order Confirmation

Skills   **CH1:** Enter and edit text; use the Show/Hide ¶ feature **CH2:** Change font and font size; use formatting tools; apply styles; align text; format paragraph and line spacing **CH3:** Create tables; format tables

Scenario   You are the sales manager for a company that sells fitness equipment. Last week, you met with a client and evaluated its need for new equipment. Create and format a letter that confirms the potential equipment order.

Steps

Student
Data Files

1   Open the student data file named **U3A2-Equipment** and save it as **U3A2-Equipment-Lastname**, but replace *Lastname* with your last name.

2   In the fifth line of the letter, replace the words *Current Date* with the current date, and in the closing, replace the words *Student Name* with your name.

3   Change the font for the entire document to 12-point Times New Roman.

4   In the first line, apply the Heading 1 style to the company name, *Fitness Providers, Inc.*

5   Modify the three lines containing Fitness Providers' contact information (address and phone number) as follows:
   a. Place the street address on the same line as the city, state, and zip code, separated by a comma and a single space. You now have two lines with company contact information, with the second line containing just the phone number.
   b. Apply the Subtitle style to the two lines of contact information.
   c. Single-space these lines and set the *spacing after* paragraphs to 0.

6   Center the company name and contact information.

7   Single-space the sender's address—beginning with the line *Ms. Sophia Treaders* and ending with the line *New York, NY 10003*—and set the *spacing after paragraphs* to 0.

8   Remove the blank lines after the salutation (*Dear Ms. Sophia Treaders:*) and after the two paragraphs ending with *memberships* and *quote*. **Hint:** *Turn on Show/Hide ¶ and delete the appropriate paragraph symbols.*

9   In the closing, add two blank lines above your name, so that there are three paragraph symbols between the line *Thank you,* and the line with your name.

10   Single space the closing, from the line with your name through the line *Sales Representative*, and set the *spacing after paragraphs* to 0.

11   Also in the closing, italicize your title, *Sales Representative*.

12   Add a table after the paragraph that ends *growth in memberships* and before the paragraph that begins *If you agree*, as follows:
   a. Insert a table that has 2 columns and 8 rows.
   b. In row 1, type and format column headings as follows:
      i   Left column: type Equipment, apply bold formatting, and align center left (vertical center and horizontal left)
      ii   Right column: type Quantity, apply bold formatting, and align center (vertical and horizontal center)
   c. In rows 2–8, type the following equipment names and quantities:
      Treadmills, 3
      Bicycles, 2
      Elliptical machines, 4
      Rowing machine, 1
      Leg press machine, 1

Mats, 5
Large balls, 5

d. Center the data in the *Quantity* column.

e. Change the font for the entire table to 11-point Arial.

f. Size the columns to fit the contents using the AutoFit button on the Table Tools Layout tab.

g. Center the table using the Center button on the Home tab.

h. Remove all table borders.

13 Save the document.

14 Print a hard copy or submit the file as directed by your instructor.

Completed Assessment 2

Fitness Providers, Inc.
120 Fifth Street, St. Louis Park, MN 55416
800-123-4567

Current Date

Ms. Sophia Treaders
Sophia's Fitness Center
2751 Broadway
New York, NY 10003

Dear Ms. Sophia Treaders:

Thank you for your interest in purchasing exercise equipment from Fitness Providers, Inc. Based on the discussion at our meeting last week, I am proposing you add the following equipment to support your anticipated growth in memberships:

Equipment	Quantity
Treadmills	3
Bicycles	2
Elliptical machines	4
Rowing machine	1
Leg press machine	1
Mats	5
Large balls	5

If you agree that these quantities are appropriate, I will follow-up with a price quote.

Thank you,

Student Name
Sales Representative

Completed
Assessment
Preview

Assessment 3 Getting-to-Know-You Flyer

Skills   **CH1:** Enter and edit text, perform a spelling and grammar check **CH2:** Change font and font size, use formatting tools, apply styles, align text, format paragraph and line spacing **CH3:** Insert SmartArt, insert media, resize media, align and format media **CH4:** Turn on and view Track Changes, make changes and add comments, accept or reject changes and review comments, send a document for editing via email, share a file for editing on OneDrive, create a PDF file *Note: The skills list may vary depending on choices made by the student.*

Scenario   Your instructor has decided it is time for you and your classmates to learn more about one another. Your assignment for the next week is to partner with a classmate and prepare a flyer introducing him or her to the rest of the class. To ensure your introduction is accurate, you will give your partner an opportunity to review, edit, and comment on the flyer. Your partner will then return the flyer to you for final editing. When your flyer is completed, you will submit it to your instructor and share it with your classmates. Include text and an image in the flyer you create, and use at least five formatting features of Word. You may choose formatting features from any of the skills you learned in this unit.

Steps, Part A

Your instructor will pair you with another student. You will interview your partner and prepare a flyer about your partner that can be shared with your instructor and classmates. Your partner will also interview you and create an informative flyer about you.

Start with a new, blank Word document or a flyer template. The flyer you create must include text and an image. Use at least five different formatting techniques and fill one page completely, without going over onto a second page. The flyer is to be informative and attractive. It should be ready for printing and posting of a hard copy, or for conversion to a PDF file and electronic posting.

Questions you may want to ask your partner to help develop content for the flyer include these:

Where were you born?
Where do you live now?
What are your favorite activities?
Where do you work and what do you do at work?
Why are you taking this class?
What are your career goals?

When you complete the flyer, save it as **U3A3-A-Flyer-Lastname**, but replace *Lastname* with your last name. Send it as an email attachment to your partner and to your instructor.

Steps, Part B

When you receive the flyer your partner has created to introduce you, take the opportunity to review and edit the content before it is shared with the class. Make all your changes in the document using Track Changes. Also add comments that you believe will be helpful as your partner makes the final modifications to the flyer. The reviewed document must contain at least two modifications to text, at least one modification to format, and at least three comments.

Save your reviewed document with the same name that your partner gave it, but change **U3A3-A** to **U3A3-B**, so the file name will be **U3A3-B-Flyer-Lastname**.

When your review is completed, send the document back to your partner and your instructor as an email attachment.

Steps, Part C

After you receive the flyer you created back from your partner, read the comments and look over the tracked changes. Make decisions about the suggested changes by using the Accept or Reject buttons on the Review tab. Delete the comments. After you complete the review, check the document for spelling errors and correct any that you find. Ensure that the formatting makes the appropriate sections stand out and that the content fits on one page only. Save the completed document using the same name your partner used when saving it in Part B, but change **U3A3-B** to **U3A3-C**, so the file name will be **U3A3-C-Flyer-Lastname**. Create a PDF version of the flyer. Save the PDF with the same name: **U3A3-C-Flyer-Lastname**.

Steps, Part D

Share the file with your classmates as directed by your instructor—for example, by attaching it to an email, posting it to OneDrive, or posting it to a course website.

Excel Chapter 1 Creating an Excel Workbook

Study Resources

Study Resources

A chapter-based presentation with audio support, Margin Tips & Hints, and other study resources are available from this ebook page.

Features Review

Features Review

The Features Review available from this ebook page presents 10 multiple-choice questions to help you reinforce your understanding of the features covered in this chapter.

 **SNAP**

If you are a SNAP user, go to your Assignments page to complete the Features Review.

Skills Review

Review 1 Setting Up a Weekly Schedule

Skills   Understand worksheet and workbook structure; use cell references; enter text, values, and dates; use the Auto Fill feature; insert and delete columns and rows; add, rename, move, and delete worksheets; insert headers and footers; and explore options for printing

Scenario You have just started a part-time job and you need to let your employer know your availability. Create a new workbook and enter your school schedule in a format that is easy to understand.

Steps

1 Create a new, blank workbook file.

2 Save the file as **C1R1-Schedule-Lastname**, but replace *Lastname* with your last name.

3 Type Weekly Schedule in cell A1.

4 Type your name in cell A2.

5 Type the current date in cell C2.

6 Type the following entries in cells A4:B4.
   Hour
   Monday

7 Type the following entries in cells A5:A6. **Note:** *Excel automatically changes* am *to* AM.
   9 am
   11 am

8 Type the following entries in cells B5:B8.
   Sociology
   Computer Applications
   Accounting
   Sports Marketing

9 Drag to select cells A5:A8 and then use Auto Fill to fill the Hour entry series.

10 Make cell B4 active and then use the fill handle to add the days of the week *Tuesday* through *Friday* to cells C4:F4.

11 Drag to select cells B5:B8 and then use Auto Fill to copy Monday's schedule to Tuesday through Friday.

12 Rename the current sheet, typing Schedule as the new name.

13 Insert a new row 7.

14 Type the following entries in cells A7:B7.
    12:30 pm
    Lunch

15 Use Auto Fill to copy the Lunch entry to cells C7:F7.

16 Change the width of columns B through F to fit the contents.

17 Add print gridlines.

18 Add a header with the sheet name and a footer with the page number.

19 Save the workbook file.

20 Click the File tab and then click the *Print* option to see how the file will look when printed.

21 Change the print orientation to landscape.

22 Print or submit the completed workbook file as directed by your instructor.

Completed Review 1

Completed
Review Preview

	A	B	C	D	E	F
			Schedule			
1	Weekly Schedule					
2	Student Name		8/29/2018			
3						
4	Hour	Monday	Tuesday	Wednesday	Thursday	Friday
5	9:00 AM	Sociology	Sociology	Sociology	Sociology	Sociology
6	11:00 AM	Computer Applications	Computer Applications	Computer Applications	Computer Applications	Computer Applications
7	12:30 PM	Lunch	Lunch	Lunch	Lunch	Lunch
8	1:00 PM	Accounting	Accounting	Accounting	Accounting	Accounting
9	3:00 PM	Sports Marketing	Sports Marketing	Sports Marketing	Sports Marketing	Sports Marketing
10						

Review 2 Making a Healthy Pizza on a Budget

Skills Understand worksheet and workbook structure; use cell references; enter text, values, and dates; use the Auto Fill feature; add, rename, move, and delete worksheets; insert headers and footers; and explore options for printing

Scenario Pizza is one of your favorite foods, but you are on a strict budget and trying to eat healthy. You wonder whether you could save money—and eat better—by making pizza instead of buying it. Create an Excel worksheet that displays the cost of making different types of healthy pizzas.

Steps

1 Create a new, blank workbook file.

2 Save the file as **C1R2-Pizza-Lastname**, but replace *Lastname* with your last name.

3 Type Healthy Pizza on a Budget in cell A1.

4 Type your name in cell A2.

5 Type the following entries in cells A4:A8:
Ingredients
Whole wheat dough
Turkey pepperoni
Part-skim mozzarella
Green peppers

6 Type the following entries in cells B4:E4:
Everything
Pepperoni
Vegetarian
Cheese

7 Type the following entries in cells B5:B8. Be sure to type the numbers exactly as shown, including the trailing zeros.
$1.50
$2.00
$3.50
$1.25

8 Select the range B5:B8 and copy the values across the rows through column E.

9 Replace the entry in cell E7, typing the new entry as $4.50.

10 Delete the entries in cells D6:E6.

11 Delete the entry in cell E8.

12 Double-click the divider line between column A and column B to resize column A.

13 Change the print orientation to landscape.

14 Rename the current sheet, typing Pizza as the new name.

15 Insert the sheet name in the header.

16 Save the workbook file.

17 Print or submit the completed workbook file as directed by your instructor.

Completed Review 2

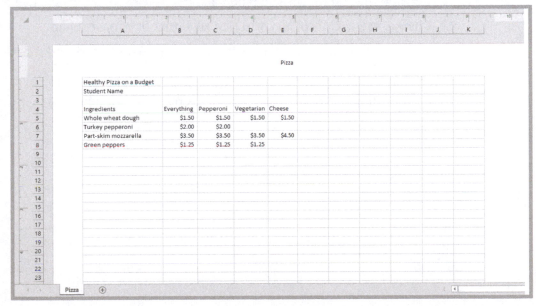

Completed
Review Preview

Review 3 **Comparing Calories**

Skills   Understand worksheet and workbook structure; use cell references; enter text, values, and dates; use the Auto Fill feature; use the spelling checker; add, rename, move, and delete worksheets; and explore options for printing

Scenario   You know vegetables are healthy but you've also heard that some have more calories than others. Create a workbook file for comparing the amount of calories in your favorite vegetables.

Steps

1   Create a new, blank workbook file.

2   Save the file as **C1R3-Vegetables-Lastname**, but replace *Lastname* with your last name.

3   Type Calory Compareson in cell A1. (Type exactly as written here. You will correct typos later.)

4   Type your name in cell A2.

5   Type Vegetable in cell A4, Measure in cell B4, and Calories in cell C4.

6   Type the following entries in cells A5:A9:
Green peas
Carrots
Cauliflower
Kale
Edamame

7   Type 1/2 cup, for the first measure, in cell B5.

8   Use Auto Fill to copy the measure from cell B5 to cells B6 through B9.

9   Type the following entries in cells C5:C9:
59
25
15
19
100

10   Check spelling in the worksheet, fixing only obvious errors and not changing any names.

11   Rename the current sheet, typing Calorie Comparison as the new name.

12   Change the size of column A so that all entries fit in the column.

13   Review the worksheet to ensure it looks like the completed worksheet shown.

14   Save the workbook file.

15   Print or submit the completed workbook file as directed by your instructor.

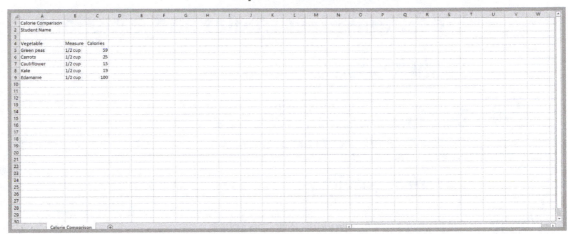

Completed Review Preview

SNAP Exercises

If you are a SNAP user, go to your SNAP Assignments page to complete additional exercises available for you.

Excel Chapter 2
Working with Formulas and Functions

Study Resources

Study Resources

A chapter-based presentation with audio support, Margin Tips & Hints, and other study resources are available from this ebook page.

Features Review

Features Review

The Features Review available from this ebook page presents 10 multiple-choice questions to help you reinforce your understanding of the features covered in this chapter.

If you are a SNAP user, go to your Assignments page to complete the Features Review.

Skills Review

Review 1 Creating a GPA Calculator

Skills   Enter a formula, enter a function, use AutoSum, use absolute and relative cell references, and copy and move cell contents

Scenario You need to maintain a 3.00 GPA to keep your scholarship. To make sure you are achieving this goal, you create a spreadsheet to track your GPA.

Steps

Student Data Files

1   Open the student data file named **C2R1-GPA**. Save the file as **C2R1-GPA-Lastname**, but replace *Lastname* with your last name.

2   Type your name in cell B3.

3   Type 85776 as your student ID in cell E5.

4   In cell D6, enter a formula that uses an absolute reference to calculate the points you earn for a course awarded the letter grade A. *Hint: Multiply the number of credits the course is worth (in row B) by the number of points awarded for the letter grade A (in cell I4).*

5   Copy the formula from cell D6 down the column for each course that received the same letter grade A.

6   In cell D9, enter a formula that uses an absolute reference to calculate the points you earn for a course awarded the letter grade B+.

7   Copy the formula from cell D9 down the column for each course that received a letter grade B+.

8   In cell D11, enter a formula that uses an absolute reference to calculate the points you earn for a course awarded the letter grade B.

9   Copy the formula from cell D9 down the column for each course that received a letter grade B.

10 In cell B14, use AutoSum to create a formula that calculates the total credits.

11 In cell D14, use a function to create a formula that calculates the total points.

12 In cell D16, enter a formula that calculates the GPA. *Hint: Divide the total number of points awarded by the total number of credits earned.*

13 Save the worksheet file.

14 Print or submit the completed worksheet as directed by your instructor.

Note: The VLOOKUP() function could be used as an alternative to the formulas you entered in column D. Refer to Excel Help for more information about the VLOOKUP() function. Check with your instructor before substituting VLOOKUP() in your worksheet for this exercise.

Completed Review 1

Completed
Review Preview

	A	B	C	D	E	F	G	H	I
1			GPA Calculator						
2								Grade	Points per Credit
3		**Name:**	Student Name		**Student ID:**	85776		A+	4.3
4								A	4
5	Courses		Credits	Grade	Points per Course			B+	3.3
6	Linear Algebra		3	A	12			B	3
7	Applied Mathematics		3	A	12			C+	2.3
8	Chemistry 101		3	A	12			C	2
9	Physics 101		3	B+	9.9			D+	1.3
10	Statistics 101		3	B+	9.9			D	1
11	Introduction to Psychology		1.5	B	4.5			F	0
12	Introduction to Sociology		1.5	B	4.5				
13	Applied Functions		3	B	9				
14		Totals	21		73.8				
15									
16				GPA	3.51				

Review 2 **Completing an Invoice**

Skills Enter a formula, enter a function, insert a function, use AutoSum, use absolute and relative cell references, copy and move cell contents, and edit cell contents

Scenario You sell security products for Endpoint, Inc. You need an invoice that totals the amount due for each item purchased based on the quantity, calculates and adds tax, and then calculates the amount of tax and invoice totals. You also need a blank version of the worksheet to use as a starting point for additional invoices.

Steps

Student
Data Files

1 Open the student data file named **C2R2-Invoice**. Save the file as **C2R2-Invoice-Lastname**, but replace *Lastname* with your last name.

2 Type your name in cell A3.

3 Change invoice number (cell B4) to *1010*.

4 In cell E4, insert a function to display the current date.

5 In cell D8, enter a formula that calculates the cost amount for the quantity purchased. Do not use a function. Copy the formula through row 13.

6 In cell E8, enter a formula that calculates the tax due using an absolute reference that refers to the tax rate in cell B5. Do not use a function. Copy the formula through row 13.

7 In cell F8, enter a formula that adds the amount and tax for the quantity purchased. Do not use a function. Copy the formula through row 13.

8. In cell E15, use a function to create a formula that calculates the total amount of tax for this order. The total should include rows 8 through 13 so that it will automatically recalculate correctly if additional items are added to the invoice at rows 12 through 13.

9. In cell F17, use a function that calculates the invoice total for cells F8 through F13.

10. Change the badge quantity to *60*.

11. Add a new sheet, Sheet2, to the workbook.

12. Select the range A1:F17 on Sheet1, copy it, and then paste it to the same range on Sheet2. Use the Paste Options button to keep the original column widths.

13. On Sheet2, clear the contents from cells B4, E4, and A8:C11 to prepare a blank invoice.

14. Rename Sheet2, typing Invoice # as its new name, and Sheet1, typing Invoice 1010 as its new name.

15. Save the workbook file.

16. Print or submit the completed workbook as directed by your instructor.

Completed Review 2, Invoice # Sheet

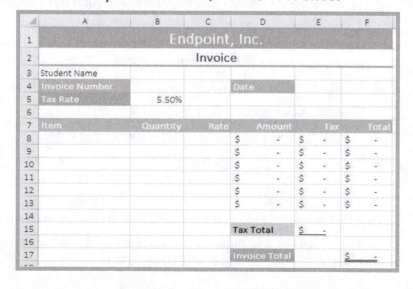

	A	B	C	D	E	F
1	Endpoint, Inc.					
2	Invoice					
3	Student Name					
4	Invoice Number	1010		Date	9/3/2018	
5	Tax Rate	5.50%				
6						
7	Item	Quantity	Rate	Amount	Tax	Total
8	Badge	60	$ 9.95	$ 597.00	$ 32.84	$ 629.84
9	Swipe Station	3	$ 299.95	$ 899.85	$ 49.49	$ 949.34
10	Management Module	1	$ 399.95	$ 399.95	$ 22.00	$ 421.95
11	Installation	1	$ 450.00	$ 450.00	$ 24.75	$ 474.75
12				$ -	$ -	$ -
13				$ -	$ -	$ -
14						
15				Tax Total	$ 129.07	
16						
17				Invoice Total		$2,475.87

Completed Review 2, Invoice 1010 Sheet

	A	B	C	D	E	F
1	Endpoint, Inc.					
2	Invoice					
3	Student Name					
4	Invoice Number			Date		
5	Tax Rate	5.50%				
6						
7	Item	Quantity	Rate	Amount	Tax	Total
8				$ -	$ -	$ -
9				$ -	$ -	$ -
10				$ -	$ -	$ -
11				$ -	$ -	$ -
12				$ -	$ -	$ -
13				$ -	$ -	$ -
14						
15				Tax Total	$ -	
16						
17				Invoice Total		$ -

Completed
Review Preview

Review 3 Calculating Your Utility Budget

Skills Enter a formula, enter a function, insert a function, use AutoSum, use absolute and relative cell references, copy and move cell contents, and use Show Formulas

Scenario Your monthly utility bill includes fixed costs (costs that are the same each month) for your mobile phone and water/sewer. It also includes variable costs (costs that are different each month) for your electricity and natural gas. Your fixed costs are projected to increase next year. You want to track your monthly utility bills and use that data to create a projected budget for next year. Complete the budget and review its formulas.

Steps

Student
Data Files

1 Open the student data file named **C2R3-UtilBudget**. Save the file as **C2R3-UtilBudget-Lastname** but replace *Lastname* with your last name.

2 On the Current Year tab, type your name in cell A2.

3 In row 9, use AutoSum and the fill handle to calculate the monthly totals for January through December.

4 In the range N5:P9, use functions to find the annual *Total*, *Average*, and *Max* values for each type of utility and the total utility amount.

5 Copy the range A1:P9 and paste it to the same range on the Projected sheet. Use the Paste Options button to keep the source column widths. Complete Steps 6–12 on the Projected sheet.

6 Change the entry in cell A3 to *Projected*.

7 Water/Sewer values are projected to increase by 5% next year. In cell C14, type 5%.

8 Mobile Phone values are projected to increase by 3% next year. In cell C15, type 3%.

9 In cell B8, enter a formula that calculates the projected Water/Sewer value. Use absolute references and parentheses where required. **Hint:** *The projected value is calculated by multiplying the previous year's value by the projected increase and then adding the previous year's value to the result.*

10 Copy the formula in cell B8 to the appropriate monthly cells in row 8.

11 In cell B5, enter a formula that calculates the projected Mobile Phone value. Use absolute references and parentheses where required. **Hint:** *The projected value is calculated by multiplying the previous year's value by the projected increase and then adding the previous year's value to the result.*

12 Copy the formula in cell B5 to the appropriate monthly cells in row 5.

13 Use Show Formulas to verify that you used absolute references and parentheses correctly in rows 5 and 8.

14 Save the workbook file.

15 Print or submit the completed workbook as directed by your instructor.

Completed Review 3, Current Year Sheet

	A	B	C	D	E	F	G	H	I	J	K	L	M	N	O	P
1	Utility Budget															
2	Student Name															
3	Current Year															
4	Utility	Jan	Feb	Mar	Apr	May	Jun	Jul	Aug	Sep	Oct	Nov	Dec	Total	Average	Max
5	Mobile Phone	$ 75.50	$ 75.50	$ 75.50	$ 75.50	$ 75.50	$ 75.50	$ 75.50	$ 75.50	$ 75.50	$ 75.50	$ 75.50	$ 75.50	$ 906.00	$ 75.50	$ 75.50
6	Electricity	$ 78.22	$ 65.21	$ 56.12	$ 44.09	$ 65.09	$ 101.99	$ 121.99	$ 92.80	$ 88.55	$ 99.04	$ 115.15	$ 99.99	$ 1,028.24	$ 85.69	$ 121.99
7	Natural Gas	$ 215.09	$ 180.99	$ 176.77	$ 39.99	$ 14.90	$ 12.50	$ 10.50	$ 10.50	$ 67.04	$ 88.50	$ 97.65	$ 201.98	$ 1,116.41	$ 93.03	$ 215.09
8	Water/Sewer	$ 22.50	$ 22.50	$ 22.50	$ 22.50	$ 22.50	$ 22.50	$ 22.50	$ 22.50	$ 22.50	$ 22.50	$ 22.50	$ 22.50	$ 270.00	$ 22.50	$ 22.50
9	Total	$ 391.31	$ 344.20	$ 330.89	$ 182.08	$ 177.99	$ 212.49	$ 230.49	$ 201.30	$ 253.59	$ 285.54	$ 310.80	$ 399.97	$ 3,320.65	$ 276.72	$ 399.97

Completed Review 3, Projected Sheet

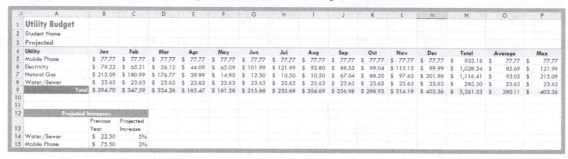

	A	B	C	D	E	F	G	H	I	J	K	L	M	N	O	P
1	Utility Budget															
2	Student Name															
3	Projected															
4	Utility	Jan	Feb	Mar	Apr	May	Jun	Jul	Aug	Sep	Oct	Nov	Dec	Total	Average	Max
5	Mobile Phone	$ 77.77	$ 77.77	$ 77.77	$ 77.77	$ 77.77	$ 77.77	$ 77.77	$ 77.77	$ 77.77	$ 77.77	$ 77.77	$ 77.77	$ 933.18	$ 77.77	$ 77.77
6	Electricity	$ 78.22	$ 65.21	$ 56.12	$ 44.09	$ 65.09	$ 101.99	$ 121.99	$ 92.80	$ 88.55	$ 99.04	$ 115.15	$ 99.99	$ 1,028.24	$ 85.69	$ 121.99
7	Natural Gas	$ 215.09	$ 180.99	$ 176.77	$ 39.99	$ 14.90	$ 12.50	$ 10.50	$ 10.50	$ 67.04	$ 88.50	$ 97.65	$ 201.98	$ 1,116.41	$ 93.03	$ 215.09
8	Water/Sewer	$ 23.63	$ 23.63	$ 23.63	$ 23.63	$ 23.63	$ 23.63	$ 23.63	$ 23.63	$ 23.63	$ 23.63	$ 23.63	$ 23.63	$ 283.50	$ 23.63	$ 23.63
9	Total	$ 394.70	$ 347.59	$ 334.28	$ 185.47	$ 181.38	$ 215.88	$ 233.88	$ 204.69	$ 256.98	$ 288.93	$ 314.19	$ 403.36	$ 3,361.33	$ 280.11	$ 403.36
10																
11																
12	Projected Increases															
13		Previous Year	Projected Increase													
14	Water/Sewer	$ 22.50	5%													
15	Mobile Phone	$ 75.50	3%													

Completed Review Preview

SNAP Exercises

SNAP

If you are a SNAP user, go to your SNAP Assignments page to complete additional exercises available for you.

Excel Chapter 3 Formatting Cells

Study Resources

Study Resources

A chapter-based presentation with audio support, Margin Tips & Hints, and other study resources are available from this ebook page.

Features Review

Features Review

The Features Review available from this ebook page presents 10 multiple-choice questions to help you reinforce your understanding of the features covered in this chapter.

If you are a SNAP user, go to your Assignments page to complete the Features Review.

Skills Review

Review 1 **Formatting a Metric Conversion Worksheet**

Skills   Apply number formats, work with other formatting tools, adjust column width and row height, add borders, and merge cells

Scenario   You have created a worksheet showing common English-Metric conversions. You need to format the worksheet so it is easy to use and read.

Steps

Student Data Files

1 Open the student data file named **C3R1-Metric** and save the file as **C3R1-Metric-Lastname**, but replace *Lastname* with your last name.

2 Type your name in cell A2.

3 Use the Page Layout tab to apply the Slice theme to the workbook. ***Hint:*** *Use the Themes button in the Themes group on the Page Layout tab.*

4 Apply the Title cell style to cell A1.

5 Merge and center cells A1:D1.

6 Apply the Accent6 cell style to cells A3:B3 and apply bold formatting.

7 Apply the Accent1 cell style to cells C3:D3 and apply bold formatting.

8 Decrease the decimals to zero decimal places in cells A4:A14.

9 Apply the Number format to cells C4:C14.

10 Apply a Thick Outside Border to cells A3:B14.

11 Apply a Thick Outside Border to cells C3:D14.

12 Change the row height of row 3 to *20*.

13 Merge and center cells A3:B3.

14 Merge and center cells C3:D3.

15 Change the width of columns B and D to *18*.

16 Save the file.

17 Print or submit the completed worksheet as directed by your instructor.

Completed Review 1

	A	B	C	D
1	Metric Conversions			
2	Student Name			
3	**English**		**Metric**	
4	5	cubic feet	0.14	cubic meters
5	10	cubic yards	7.65	cubic meters
6	10	feet	3.05	meters
7	1	gallons	3.79	liters
8	12	inches	30.48	centimeters
9	2	miles	3.22	kilometers
10	25	pounds	9.33	kilograms
11	40	square feet	3.72	square meters
12	12	square miles	31.08	square kilometers
13	10	square yards	8.36	square meters
14	5	yards	4.57	meters
15				

Completed
Review Preview

Review 2 Formatting Stock Portfolio Information

Skills   Apply number formats, work with other formatting tools, adjust column width and row height, apply conditional formatting, add borders, and merge cells

Scenario   You track a portfolio of stocks and other securities using an online service such as Yahoo! Finance. You are able to download daily quote data, but it downloads in a raw, unformatted version that makes it difficult to review. Apply formatting to make the downloaded data more attractive and useful.

Steps

Student
Data Files

1 Open the student data file named **C3R2-Quotes** and save the file as **C3R2-Quotes-Lastname**, but replace *Lastname* with your last name.

2 Type your name in cell A15.

3 Delete column D, which holds time information.

4 Insert two new rows at the top of the sheet and then type Quotes in cell A1.

5 Apply the Title cell style to cell A1.

6 Merge and center the contents of cells A1:G1.

7 Apply the Currency format to the cells in the *Closing Price*, *Change*, *Low*, and *High* columns.

8 Use Conditional Formatting to display cells in the *Change* column that are less than 0 with a Light Red fill with Dark Red Text.

9 Apply the Comma Style format to the cells in the *Volume* column and then display the values with 0 decimal places. ***Hint:*** *Use the Comma Style button in the Number group on the Home tab.*

10 Apply the Accent5 cell style to the range A3:G3, and bold and center the text.

11 AutoFit column B.

12 Apply a Bottom Border to cells A4:G4.

13 Use the Format Painter to copy the formatting from A4:G4 to A5:G15.

14 Change the height for row 2 to 6.00, and apply the 20% - Accent2 cell style to cells A2:G2.

15 Display data bars in the Volume column. Apply the Orange Data Bar Gradient Fill.

16 Save the file.

17 Print or submit the completed worksheet as directed by your instructor.

Completed Review 2

Completed
Review Preview

	A	B	C	D	E	F	G
1				Quotes			
3	Ticker	Closing Price	Date	Change	Low	High	Volume
4	AAPL	$115.68	8/5	$0.91	$112.10	$117.44	87,408,168
5	AFL	$64.24	8/5	$0.31	$64.09	$64.78	828,340
6	CREE	$24.99	8/5	$0.21	$25.55	$24.87	883,023
7	CSCO	$28.28	8/5	$0.26	$28.10	$28.60	12,745,582
8	CSX	$30.85	8/5	-$0.02	$30.81	$31.26	2,690,625
9	F	$14.78	8/5	-$0.13	$14.72	$15.04	15,708,362
10	GE	$26.13	8/5	$0.23	$26.03	$26.33	16,416,197
11	GOOG	$645.45	8/5	$0.16	$633.16	$647.86	1,569,619
12	MSFT	$47.76	8/5	$0.22	$47.64	$48.41	18,318,392
13	SPH	$36.66	8/5	$0.01	$36.13	$37.27	160,775
14	TLT	$121.66	8/5	$0.91	$121.19	$121.91	5,643,251
15	WFC	$57.72	8/5	$0.11	$57.48	$58.02	8,443,810
16							
17	Student Name						

Review 3 **Creating an Income Statement**

Skills Apply number formats, work with other formatting tools, adjust column width and row height, add borders, and merge cells

Scenario You run a small computer company and need to prepare an income statement to track your revenues and expenses so that you can determine how well your business has performed over the past three years. You have entered the necessary data but need to finish the income statement worksheet by formatting it.

Steps

Student
Data Files

1 Open the student data file named **C3R3-Income** and save the file as **C3R3-Income-Lastname**, but replace *Lastname* with your last name.

2 Type your name in cell A20 and then press Enter.

3 Use the Page Layout tab to apply the Ion Boardroom theme to the workbook. ***Hint:*** *Use the Themes button in the Themes group on the Page Layout tab.*

4 Apply the Title cell style to cell A1.

5 Merge and center cells A1:D1, A2:D2, and A3:D3.

6 Select the range A2:D3, apply the 20% - Accent4 cell style, and add a Thick Outside border.

7 Apply the Accent4 cell style and Bold formatting to cells A5:D5.

8 Use Merge Across to merge cells A6:D6 and A11:D11.

9 Apply the 20% - Accent4 cell style to cells A6 and A11.

10 Apply the Accounting format with no decimal places to the values for each year and the totals.

11 Apply a Top and Bottom border to cells A10:D10 and A17:D17.

12 Apply Double Underline format to cells B18:D18. *Hint*: *Use the Underline arrow in the Font group on the Home tab.*

13 Increase the height of row 1 to 30.

14 Delete row 4.

15 Apply a Thick Bottom Border to cells A5:D5 and A10:D10.

16 Save the file.

17 Print or submit the completed file as directed by your instructor.

Completed Review 3

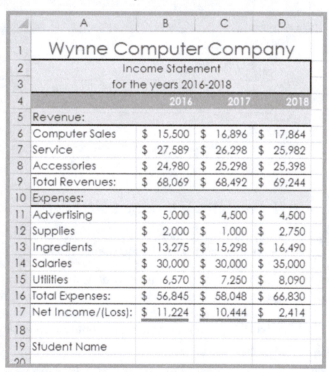

Completed
Review Preview

SNAP Exercises

If you are a SNAP user, go to your SNAP Assignments page to complete additional exercises available for you.

Excel Chapter 4 **Working with Charts**

Study Resources

Study Resources

A chapter-based presentation with audio support, Margin Tips & Hints, and other study resources are available from this ebook page.

Features Review

Features Review

The Features Review available from this ebook page presents 10 multiple-choice questions to help you reinforce your understanding of the features covered in this chapter.

 **SNAP**

If you are a SNAP user, go to your Assignments page to complete the Features Review.

Skills Review

Review 1 **Charting Budget Data**

Skills Add and edit chart labels, create a pie chart, and modify a pie chart

Scenario You have created a monthly budget to manage your finances. You have organized your spending into the categories rent, entertainment, food, car, and savings. Create a pie chart to show how much you are spending on each budget category.

Steps

Student Data Files

1 Open the student data file named **C4R1-Budget** and save the file as **C4R1-Budget-Lastname**, but replace *Lastname* with your last name.

2 Type your name in cell A10.

3 Create a 3-D pie chart using the data in A3:B7.

4 Type Monthly Budget in the chart title placeholder.

5 Add data labels at the Inside End position. Display the data labels as percentages and show the category name. **Hint:** *Click the* Category Name *check box to insert a check mark.*

6 Remove the legend. **Hint:** *Click the Add Chart Element button in the Chart Layouts group on the Chart Tools Design tab, click the* Legend *option in the drop-down list, and then click the* None *option in the second drop-down list.*

7 Move the chart so that its top left corner covers cell D2.

8 Explode the *Rent* slice.

9 Change the chart style to *Style 2*. **Hint:** *Chart styles are listed in numeric order and the style name displays as a ScreenTip when you point to a style.*

10 Change the page orientation for the entire worksheet to landscape.

11 Save the file.

12 Print or submit the completed file as directed by your instructor.

Completed Review 1

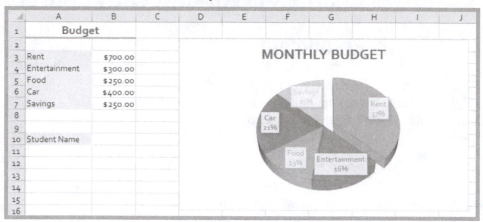

Review 2 Comparing Temperatures

Skills   Create a line chart, modify chart data, and add and edit chart labels

Scenario You are deciding where and when to go on your next vacation. You have charted the average monthly temperature in two cities to help you make your decision. You create a line chart to illustrate the differences in temperature.

Steps

Student
Data Files

1   Open the student data file named **C4R2-Temperature** and save the file as **C4R2-Temperature-Lastname**, but replace *Lastname* with your last name.

2   Insert a 2-D Line with Markers chart using the data in A3:C15.

3   Move the line chart to a new sheet.

4   Type Average Monthly Temperatures in the chart title placeholder.

5   Type Months as the title of the horizontal axis. ***Hint:*** *Click the Add Chart Element button in the Chart Layouts group on the Chart Tools Design tab, click the* Axis Titles *option in the drop-down list, click the* Primary Horizontal *option in the second drop-down list, type* Months, *and then press Enter.*

6   Type Temperature in Degrees as the title of the vertical axis. Use the hint in the previous step but click *Primary Vertical* instead of *Primary Horizontal*.

7   Use the Chart Tools Design tab to change to the Style 4 chart style. ***Hint:*** *Chart styles are listed in numeric order and the style name displays a ScreenTip when you point to a style.*

8   Save the file.

9   Print or submit the completed workbook file as directed by your instructor.

Completed Review 2

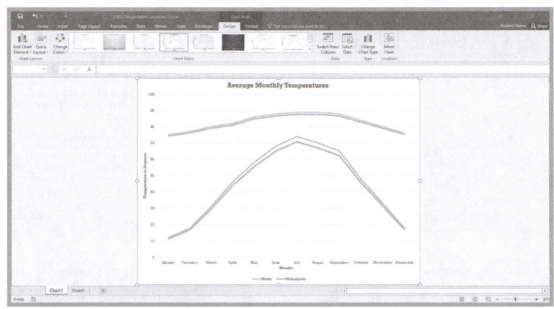

**Completed
Review Preview**

Review 3 **Charting Sales**

Skills   Create a column chart, modify chart data, and add and edit chart labels

Scenario   You manage a sales team. You have sales numbers, by employee, for the first quarter through fourth quarter of this year. You create a column chart to compare sales levels among your employees.

Steps

**Student
Data Files**

1   Open the student data file named **C4R3-Sales** and save the file as **C4R3-Sales-Lastname**, but replace *Lastname* with your last name.

2   Select the quarterly sales data for all four salespeople along with the column titles.

3   Insert a 3-D Clustered Column chart that displays the data you selected in Step 2. **Hint**: *The 3-D Clustered Column is the first option in the 3-D section of the Insert Column or Bar Chart drop-down gallery.*

4   Move the chart so the upper left corner is aligned with cell B9.

5   Type Sales Performance to replace the chart title placeholder. If requested by your instructor, save the file at this point and submit it.

6   Andre Perez has left the company. Remove his sales data from the chart data series. **Hint**: *Change the chart data series to remove Andre Perez from the column chart.*

7   Click the Switch Row/Column button in the Data group on the Chart Tools Design tab. Notice how this switches the way the data is plotted. The employee names now appear on the horizontal axis instead of the sales quarters.

8   Change to the Color 2 option in the *Colorful* section of the Change Colors drop-down gallery.

9   Change the chart layout to Layout 5. **Hint**: *Click the Quick Layout button in the Chart Layouts group on the Chart Tools Design tab, point to the fifth option in the drop-down gallery, confirm that the ScreenTip says* Layout 5, *and then click the option.*

10 Type Sales to replace the axis title placeholder text.

11 Save the file.

12 Print or submit the completed file as directed by your instructor.

Completed Review 3

Completed
Review Preview

SNAP Exercises

*If you are a SNAP user, go to your SNAP Assignments page
to complete additional exercises available for you.*

Unit 4 **Excel**

Skills Assessment

Assessment 1 **Charting Population Statistics**

Skills   **CH1:** Understand worksheet and workbook structure; use cell references; enter text, values, and dates; add, rename, move, and delete worksheets; explore options for printing **CH2:** Enter a formula; enter a function; edit cell contents; use Show Formulas **CH3:** Work with other formatting tools; adjust column width and row height; merge cells **CH4:** Create a column chart; add and edit chart labels

Scenario   You are working in a marketing department. Your company is going to test market a new product to see if it sells. The marketing campaign will initially target the six largest cities in the United States. You have been asked to prepare a spreadsheet and chart that show the population in these cities.

Steps

1   Open a blank workbook in Excel and name it **U4A1-Population-Lastname**, but replace *Lastname* with your last name.

2   Type Population Statistics in cell A1.

3   Merge and center cells A1:C1.

4   Format cell A1 with the Heading 1 cell style.

5   Change the theme to Vapor Trail. **Hint:** *You may need to scroll down to locate this option in the Themes drop-down gallery.*

6   Type the following data in cells A3:C9:

City	State	Population
New York	New York	7,491,079
Los Angeles	California	3,928,864
Chicago	Illinois	2,722,389
Houston	Texas	2,239,558
Philadelphia	Pennsylvania	1,560,297
Phoenix	Arizona	1,537,058

7   In cell B11, type Total.

8   In cell B12, type Minimum.

9   In cell B13, type Maximum.

10   Right align and bold the labels in B11:B13.

11   Use the appropriate function to insert the total population for the listed cities in cell C11.

12   Use the appropriate function to insert the lowest population in cell C12.

13   Edit the population for New York, New York to read *8,491,079*.

14   Use the appropriate function to insert the highest population in cell C13.

15   AutoFit columns A, B, and C.

16   Select cells A3:C3 and then format the cells with the Accent5 cell style.

17   Select cells A3:A9 and cells C3:C9 and then insert a 3-D Clustered Column chart. **Hint:** *Use the Ctrl key to select the nonadjacent range.*

18 Change the chart style to Style 2.

19 Move the chart so that the top left corner of the chart is in cell E2.

20 Change the name of Sheet 1, typing Population as the new name.

21 Change the page orientation for the entire worksheet to landscape.

22 Save the workbook file.

23 Print a copy of the worksheet or submit the completed file as directed by your instructor.

24 Show formulas in the worksheet.

25 Print a copy of the worksheet or submit the completed file as directed by your instructor.
    Note: *You have now printed a copy showing data and then another copy showing formulas.*

Completed Assessment 1, Step 23

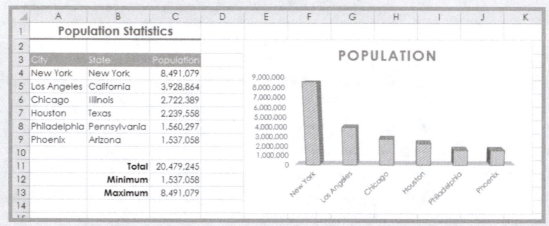

Completed
Assessment
Preview

Assessment 2 Charting Calories Burned During Exercise

Skills   **CH1:** Understand worksheet and workbook structure; enter text, values, and dates; use the spelling checker; insert headers and footers; explore options for printing **CH3:** Apply number formats; work with other formatting tools; adjust column width and row height; apply conditional formatting; merge cells **CH4:** Create a column chart; add and edit chart labels; modify chart data

Scenario You are researching an article for *Guidelines for Healthy Living Magazine*. You want to show readers how they can burn calories while on vacation without having to go to the gym. You create a worksheet with a column chart that shows examples of calories burned, noting that calories burned are affected by body weight.

Steps

Student
Data Files

1 Open the student data file named **U4A2-Exercise** and save the file as **U4A2-Exercise-Lastname**, but replace *Lastname* with your last name.

2 Merge and center cells A1:D1.

3 Format cell A1 with the Heading 1 cell style.

4 Merge and center cells B2:D2.

5 Apply the Accent4 cell style and bold formatting to cell B2.

6 Apply the Accent6 cell style to cell A3.

7 Apply the Accent1 cell style to cells B3:D3.

8. Make cell A1 active and then spell check the worksheet, ignoring all suggestions to change the abbreviation *lbs* and accepting the suggested changes to correct the two spelling errors.

9. Insert a function to enter today's date in cell A11 and apply the Long Date format.

10. Right align cells B3:D3.

11. Change the width of columns B, C, and D to 10.00 (75 pixels).

12. Change the height of row 1 to 24.00 (32 pixels).

13. Use conditional formatting to display data bars in cells B4:D8 with the *Gradient Fill Orange Data Bar* option.

14. Select the range A3:D8 and then insert a 2-D Clustered Column chart.

15. Type Calories Burned to replace the chart title placeholder.

16. Move the chart so that the top left corner of the chart is in cell F2.

17. Change the chart style to *Style 9*.

18. Add a title to the vertical axis (Primary Vertical axis), typing Calories as the new title.

19. Add a title to the horizontal axis (Primary Horizontal axis), typing Exercise as the new title.

20. Remove the Windsurfing data from the chart

21. Type your name in cell A10.

22. Insert the file name in the header and then return to Normal view.

23. Change the page orientation to landscape for the entire worksheet.

24. Save the worksheet.

25. Print a copy of the worksheet or submit the completed file as directed by your instructor.

Completed Assessment 2

Completed
Assessment
Preview

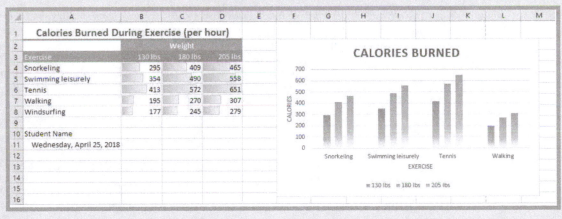

Assessment 3 Charting Employee Salary Calculations

Skills **CH1:** Understand worksheet and workbook structure; use cell references; enter text, values, and dates; add, rename, move, and delete worksheets; explore options for printing **CH2:** Enter a formula; enter a function; insert a function; use AutoSum; use absolute and relative cell references; copy and paste cell contents **CH3:** Apply number formats; work with other formatting tools; adjust column width and row height; add borders; merge cells **CH4:** Add and edit chart labels; create a pie chart; modify a pie chart

Scenario You are in charge of calculating the payroll for the employees at Paradigm Steel. The employees receive a base salary plus commission. You need to calculate new salary figures for all the employees because all employees will receive a 5.25 percent raise. You use a pie chart to display the results in an easy-to-read format.

Steps

Student
Data Files

1 Open the student data file named **U4A3-Steel** and save the file as **U4A3-Steel-Lastname**, but replace *Lastname* with your last name.

2 Change the width of column A to 22.00 (181 pixels). Change the width of column B to 13.00 (109 pixels).

3 Change the width of columns C through G to 16.00 (133 pixels).

4 Type the title Commission in cell E2.

5 In cell E3, calculate the commission using a formula that multiplies projected sales by the commission rate. *Hint: Use an absolute reference for cell B18.* Copy the formula in cell E3 to cells E4:E12.

6 Type the title Salary in cell F2.

7 In cell F3, calculate the salary by adding the base salary and the commission. Copy the formula in cell F3 to cells F4:F12.

8 Type the title New Salary in cell G2.

9 Employees will all receive a 5.25 percent raise on their base salary. In cell G3, calculate the new salary using the formula Base Salary + (Base Salary * 5.25%) + Commission. Copy the formula in cell G3 to cells G4:G12.

10 Apply the Currency format with no decimal places to the values in columns C through G.

11 Set the height of rows 13 through 16 to 22.50 (30 pixels).

12 Right align the *Total*, *Average*, *Lowest*, and *Highest* labels and apply bold formatting. Move these labels from cells A13:A16 to cells B13:B16.

13 Use the appropriate function to calculate the *Total*, *Average*, *Highest*, and *Lowest* values for columns C through G.

14 Merge and center cells A1:G1 and set the row height of row 1 to 48.00 (64 pixels).

15 Apply the Title cell style to cell A1.

16 Set the row height of row 2 to 20.25 (27 pixels).

17 Center the column headings in row 2, apply the Accent5 cell style, and apply bold formatting.

18 Add a thick outside border around the column headings in row 2.

19 Apply the Accent2 cell style to cells C13:G13, Accent3 style to cells C14:G14, Accent4 cell style to cells C15:G15, and Accent5 cell style to cells C16:G16.

20 Type your name in cell A20.

21 Change the page orientation to landscape.

22 Create a 3-D pie chart of the new salaries for all employees. *Hint: Use the Ctrl key to highlight A2:A12 and G2:G12 before creating the chart.*

23 Move the location of the chart to a new sheet and rename the sheet, typing Salary Chart as the new name.

24 Change the chart style to Style 2.

25 Use the Chart Elements button to add data labels that display the category name at the Inside End position along with the already displayed salary value. Remove the legend from the chart.

26 Modify the chart title, typing EMPLOYEE 2018 SALARIES as the new chart title.

27 Rename Sheet1, typing Data as the new sheet name.

28 Save the workbook.

29 Print a copy of the worksheet and the chart sheet or submit the completed workbook as directed by your instructor.

Completed Assessment 3 Data

	A	B	C	D	E	F	G
1				Paradigm Steel Company			
2	Employee	Hire Date	Base Salary	Projected Sales	Commission	Salary	New Salary
3	Chronowski, John	10/12/2009	$66,950	$422,165	$13,720	$80,670	$84,906
4	Mandinka Al-Jab Bar	12/14/2014	$50,250	$323,912	$10,527	$60,777	$63,968
5	McDonald Jack	10/25/2013	$49,581	$238,584	$7,754	$57,335	$60,345
6	Meeks Tyrone	6/13/2007	$62,500	$342,413	$11,128	$73,628	$77,494
7	Putin, Nikita	5/24/2009	$59,500	$750,450	$24,390	$83,890	$88,294
8	Adley, Martha	4/11/2016	$46,253	$384,616	$12,500	$58,753	$61,838
9	Damato, Michelle	5/13/2015	$57,157	$489,401	$15,906	$73,063	$76,898
10	DeJesus, Gino	2/10/2009	$64,219	$599,689	$19,490	$83,709	$88,104
11	Flynn, Georgeana	3/20/2012	$91,821	$619,984	$20,149	$111,970	$117,849
12	Frost, Leonard	11/19/2017	$71,272	$338,914	$11,015	$82,287	$86,607
13		Total	$619,503	$4,510,128	$146,579	$766,082	$806,301
14		Average	$61,950	$451,013	$14,658	$76,608	$80,630
15		Lowest	$46,253	$238,584	$7,754	$57,335	$60,345
16		Highest	$91,821	$750,450	$24,390	$111,970	$117,849
17							
18	Commission Rate	3.25%					
19							
20	Student Name						

Completed Assessment 3 Salary Chart

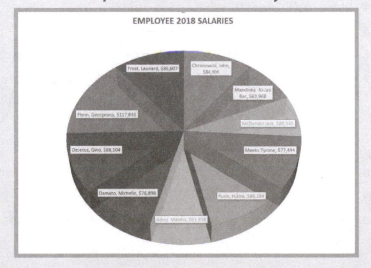

Completed Assessment Preview

Access Chapter 1 **Working with Databases**

Study Resources

Study Resources

A chapter-based presentation with audio support, Margin Tips & Hints, and other study resources are available from this ebook page.

Features Review

Features Review

The Features Review available from this ebook page presents 10 multiple-choice questions to help you reinforce your understanding of the features covered in this chapter.

If you are a SNAP user, go to your Assignments page to complete the Features Review.

Skills Review

Review 1 **Updating and Sorting an Organic Food Store Database**

Skills   Open and navigate a database, enter data, edit data, and sort data

Scenario   You are in charge of updating the records in a database for an organic food store. You add some new items to the database and edit an existing record. You also sort a datasheet to make it easier to find information in the table.

Steps

Student Data Files

1 Open the student data file named **C1R1-OrganicProducts**. If a security warning appears immediately below the ribbon, click the Enable Content button. If a second security warning appears, click the Yes button.

2 Open the Customers table.

3 In record 3, edit the contents of the *LastName* field to *Katz* instead of *Kati*.

4 Close the Customers table.

5 Open the Products form.

6 On the Record Navigation bar, click the New (blank) record button.

7 Add the following information to create three new records:

ProductNo	ProductName	AllergenInfo
5172	Ancient Grains Cereal	wheat
8322	Organic Cottage Cheese	milk
8347	Organic Cream Cheese	milk

8 Close the Products form.

9 Open the Inventory table.

10 Add the following information to create three new records:

ProductNo	Quantity
5172	87
8322	98
8347	103

11 Sort the Inventory table by the *Quantity* field in ascending order.

12 Save the Inventory table without closing it. ***Hint:*** *Click the Save button on the Quick Access Toolbar.*

13 Print the Inventory table or submit the completed database as directed by your instructor.

14 Remove the sort and save the Inventory table again.

15 Close the Inventory table and then the database.

Completed Review 1, Step 3

CustomerID	FirstName	LastName	Address	City	State	ZIP	Click to Add
1001	Jean-Claude	Gital	1325 Ocean Dri	Boca Raton	FL	33002-	
1002	Cassandra	Inez	309 Lakeside R	Chicago	IL	60633-	
1003	Nathan	Katz	812 Tibia Lane	Palm Springs	CA	80987-	
1004	Brenda	Newcombe	2 Wentworth C	Wellington	FL	38992-	

Completed Review 1, Step 7

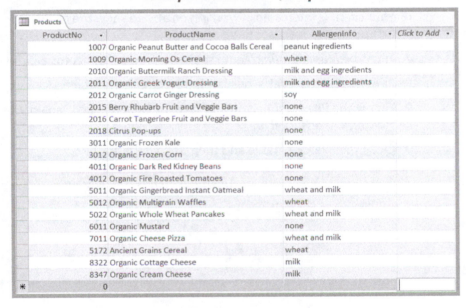

ProductNo	ProductName	AllergenInfo	Click to Add
1007	Organic Peanut Butter and Cocoa Balls Cereal	peanut ingredients	
1009	Organic Morning Os Cereal	wheat	
2010	Organic Buttermilk Ranch Dressing	milk and egg ingredients	
2011	Organic Greek Yogurt Dressing	milk and egg ingredients	
2012	Organic Carrot Ginger Dressing	soy	
2015	Berry Rhubarb Fruit and Veggie Bars	none	
2016	Carrot Tangerine Fruit and Veggie Bars	none	
2018	Citrus Pop-ups	none	
3011	Organic Frozen Kale	none	
3012	Organic Frozen Corn	none	
4011	Organic Dark Red Kidney Beans	none	
4012	Organic Fire Roasted Tomatoes	none	
5011	Organic Gingerbread Instant Oatmeal	wheat and milk	
5012	Organic Multigrain Waffles	wheat	
5022	Organic Whole Wheat Pancakes	wheat and milk	
6011	Organic Mustard	none	
7011	Organic Cheese Pizza	wheat and milk	
5172	Ancient Grains Cereal	wheat	
8322	Organic Cottage Cheese	milk	
8347	Organic Cream Cheese	milk	
0			

Completed Review 1, Step 11

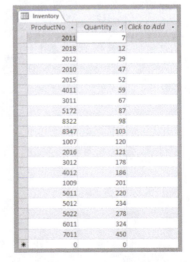

ProductNo	Quantity	Click to Add
2011	7	
2018	12	
2012	29	
2010	47	
2015	52	
4011	59	
3011	67	
5172	87	
8322	98	
8347	103	
1007	120	
2016	121	
3012	178	
4012	186	
1009	201	
5011	220	
5012	234	
5022	278	
6011	324	
7011	450	
0	0	

Completed
Review Preview

Review 2 **Filtering a Database of Exercises**

Skills   Open and navigate a database, filter data, and use existing queries and reports

Scenario   You are a personal trainer. You have created a database of exercises so that you can easily develop exercise plans for your clients. You are working with a new client, and you filter the records and run existing queries to provide your client with exercise options.

Steps

Student Data Files

1   Open the student data file named **C1R2-Exercises**. If a security warning appears immediately below the ribbon, click the Enable Content button. If a second security warning appears, click the Yes button.

2   Open the No Equipment Required query to display all the exercises that do not require exercise equipment.

3   Close the No Equipment Required query.

4   Open the Strength Exercises query to display all of the exercises designed for strength training.

5   Close the Strength Exercises query.

6   Your client is interested in working on abs. To show the client appropriate exercise options, first open the Exercises table.

7   Filter the *MuscleGroup* column so that only the Abs records are displayed.

8   Print the Exercises table or submit the completed database as directed by your instructor.

9   Toggle the filter to turn it off and save the Exercises table again. **Hint:** *Click the Save button in the Quick Access Toolbar*.

10   Close the Exercises table and then the database.

Completed Review 2, Step 2

Completed Review 2, Step 4

Completed Review Preview

Completed Review 2, Step 7

Review 3 **Tracking Community Volunteers**

Skills Open and navigate a database, sort data, format a datasheet, and use existing queries and reports

Scenario You work in the student records office at your school and have set up a database to track student community service hours. This data is important because many students volunteer to meet graduation or financial aid requirements. To make the data easy for others in your office to use, you sort the database, format a datasheet, and display a report.

Steps

Student Data Files

1 Open the student data file named **C1R3-CommunityService**. If a security warning appears immediately below the ribbon, click the Enable Content button. If a second security warning appears, click the Yes button.

2 Open the Organizations report to display information about the community agencies at which students can volunteer.

3 Close the Organizations report.

4 Open the Volunteer Hours table.

5 Change the font size to 12 points.

6 Center the entries in the fields of the *ServiceDate* column.

7 Sort the table by the *OrganizationName* column in ascending order.

8 Save the changes to the Volunteer Hours table without closing it. **Hint:** *Click the Save button in the Quick Access Toolbar.*

9 Print the Volunteer Hours table or submit the completed file as directed by your instructor.

10 Close the Volunteer Hours table and then the database.

Completed Review 3, Step 2

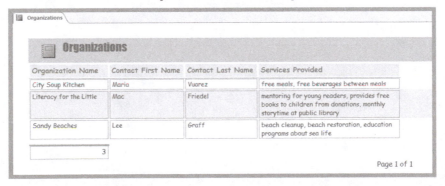

Completed Review Preview

Completed
Review Preview

SNAP Exercises

 **SNAP**   *If you are a SNAP user, go to your SNAP Assignments page to complete additional exercises available for you.*

Access Chapter 2 **Creating Forms and Tables**

Study Resources

Study
Resources

A chapter-based presentation with audio support, Margin Tips & Hints, and other study resources are available from this ebook page.

Features Review

Features
Review

The Features Review available from this ebook page presents 10 multiple-choice questions to help you reinforce your understanding of the features covered in this chapter.

If you are a SNAP user, go to your Assignments page to complete the Features Review.

Skills Review

Review 1   **Adding to the Database for an Organic Food Store**

Skills   Create a table, enter data in a table, create a form, and enter data in a form

Scenario   You are in charge of updating a database for an organic food store. You need to add a new table to the existing database. The table will store information about upcoming product promotions. You also need to add data to the new table.

Steps

Student
Data Files

1 Open the student data file named **C2R1-OrganicProducts**. If a security warning appears immediately below the ribbon, click the Enable Content button. If a second security warning appears, click the Yes button.

2 Create a new table in Design view.

3 Add the following three fields to the table:

Field Name	Data Type
ProductNo	Number
Event	Short Text
Discount	Currency

4 Make the *ProductNo* field the primary key.

5 Save the table, typing Events as the table name.

6 Close the Events table.

7 Create a form based on the Events table.

8 Save the form, accepting the form name *Events*.

9 Open the Events form in Form view and then add three new records containing the following information. ***Hint:** Press the Tab key after each entry.*

ProductNo	Event	Discount
2018	Summer Cool-off	1.00
3011	Product Launch	0.75
3012	Product Launch	0.50

10 Close the Events form.

11 Open the Events table.

12 Copy the first record, which has the product number 2018.

13 Paste the copied record as the fourth record.

14 Change the *ProductNo* entry for the fourth record, typing 2015 as the new entry.

15 Adjust the width of the Event column in the datasheet so that all the data is visible.

16 Save the database.

17 Print the Events table or submit the completed database as directed by your instructor.

18 Close the Events table and then the database.

Completed Review 1, Events Form

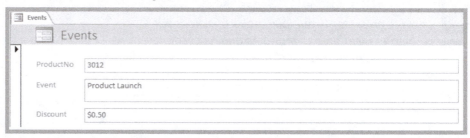

Completed Review 1, Events Table

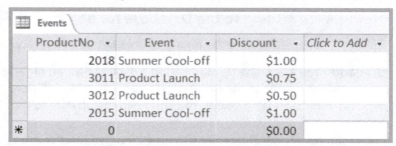

Completed
Review Preview

Review 2 **Expanding an Exercises Database**

Skills   Create a table, enter data in a table, create a form, and enter data in a form

Scenario You are a personal trainer. You need to expand your existing database to include a table with client contact information. To make entering client data easier, you specify values for the *Schedule* field and create a form.

Steps

Student
Data Files

1 Open the student data file named **C2R2-Exercises**. If a security warning appears immediately below the ribbon, click the Enable Content button. If a second security warning appears, click the Yes button.

2 Create a new table in Design view.

3 Add the following five fields to the table:

Field Name	Data Type
ClientID	AutoNumber
LastName	Short Text
FirstName	Short Text
Email	Short Text
Schedule	Lookup Wizard

4 In the Lookup Wizard dialog box, specify your own values in a single column, typing the following entries:
Orientation
Daily
Two times a week
Three times a week

When you are done, click the Finish button to apply your entries and close the dialog box.

5 Make the *ClientID* field the primary key.

6 Save the table, typing Clients as the table name.

7 Close the table.

8 Create a form based on the Clients table.

9 Switch to Design view and then narrow the width of the fields in the form by dragging the right border of the *ClientID* field to the 5-inch mark on the ruler.

10 Save the form, typing Clients as the form name.

11 Switch to Form view.

12 Add three new records containing the following information. ***Note***: *Press Tab in the* ClientID *field to enter an AutoNumber.*

LastName	FirstName	Email	Schedule
Wilson	Joe	jwilson@ParadigmCollege.net	Orientation
Ryan	Mariah	mryan@ParadigmCollege.net	Daily
Perez	Andrea	aperez@ParadigmCollege.net	Daily

13 Close the form.

14 Open the Clients table and AutoFit the *Email* field.

15 Close the form.

16 Print the Clients table or submit the completed database as directed by your instructor.

17 Close the Clients table and then the database.

Completed Review 2, Clients Form

Completed Review 2, Clients Table

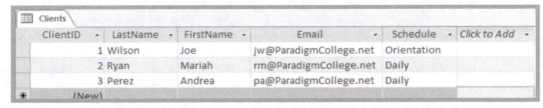

Completed
Review Preview

Review 3 Tracking Community Service Hours

Skills Create a form

Scenario You have created a database to track hours that students spend doing community service. In this exercise, you create forms to make it easier to enter data in two of the tables in the database.

Steps

Student Data Files

1 Open the student data file named **C2R3-CommunityService**. If a security warning appears immediately below the ribbon, click the Enable Content button. If a second security warning appears, click the Yes button.

2 Create a form based on the Volunteer Hours table.

3 Switch to Design view and then narrow the width of the fields in the form by dragging the right border of the *DonationID* field to the 5-inch mark on the ruler.

4 Save the form, naming it *Volunteer Hours*.

5 Switch to *Layout View*.

6 Add the date and time to the form header, accepting the default settings in the Date and Time dialog box.

7 Save the updated form.

8 Create a form based on the Organizations table.

9 Save the form, naming it *Organizations*.

10 Create a form based on the Students table.

11 Save the form, naming it *Students*.

12 Close all three open forms and then close the database.

Completed Review 3, Volunteer Hours Form

Completed Review 3, Organizations Form

Completed Review Preview

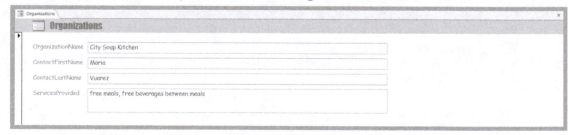

**Completed
Review Preview**

SNAP Exercises

 *If you are a SNAP user, go to your SNAP Assignments page
to complete additional exercises available for you.*

Access Chapter 3
Working with Queries and Reports

Study Resources

Study Resources

A chapter-based presentation with audio support, Margin Tips & Hints, and other study resources are available from this ebook page.

Features Review

Features Review

The Features Review available from this ebook page presents 10 multiple-choice questions to help you reinforce your understanding of the features covered in this chapter.

If you are a SNAP user, go to your Assignments page to complete the Features Review.

Skills Review

Review 1 Inventory Check—Querying an Organic Products Database

Skills Create a query in Design view, use more than one table in a query, and create and preview a report

Scenario You are the purchaser for a large grocery store and you need to find out which organic products to reorder this week. You query the organic products database to find this information.

Steps

Student Data Files

1 Open the student data file named **C3R1-OrganicProducts**. If a security warning appears immediately below the ribbon, click the Enable Content button. If a second security warning appears, click the Yes button.

2 Use Design view to create a query using data from the Products table and the Inventory table.

3 Define the query to find all products with less than 100 items in stock and to display the *ProductNo, ProductName,* and *Quantity* fields, in that order.

4 Save the query, typing Inventory under 100 as the query name. Run the query to confirm that it is selecting the correct records.

5 Close the Inventory under 100 query.

6 In the Navigation pane, click *Inventory under 100* in the Queries group.

7 Using the Report button, create a report based on the Inventory under 100 query.

8 Apply the Integral theme to the report.

9 AutoFit the *Record Count* cell. ***Hint:*** *The name of the cell appears in a ScreenTip.*

10 Save the report, naming it *Inventory under 100.*

11 Print the Inventory under 100 report or submit the completed database as directed by your instructor.

12 Close the Inventory under 100 report and then the database.

Completed Review 1, Inventory under 100 Query

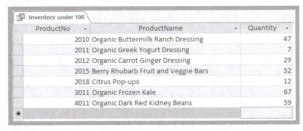

Completed Review 1, Inventory under 100 Report

Completed
Review Preview

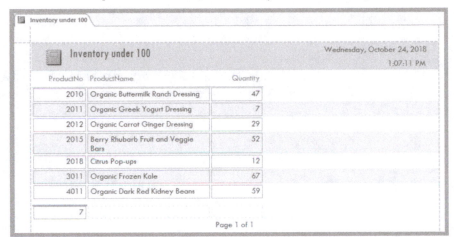

Review 2 Finding Information in an Exercises Database

Skills Use the Query Wizard and use the Report Wizard

Scenario You are a personal trainer and are preparing to send an email reminding your clients of the many exercises they can do without any equipment. You will query the Exercises database to find the contact information for your clients. You also create a report named No Equipment Required based on an existing query in the database.

Steps

Student
Data Files

1 Open the student data file named **C3R2-Exercises**. If a security warning appears immediately below the ribbon, click the Enable Content button. If a second security warning appears, click the Yes button.

2 In the Navigation pane, click *Clients* in the Tables group.

3 Use the Query Wizard to create a simple query that lists the *LastName*, *FirstName*, and *Email* fields, in that order.

4 Save the query, naming it *Clients Query*.

5 AutoFit the *Email* column.

6 Save and then close the Clients Query query.

7 In the Navigation pane, click *No Equipment Required* in the Queries group.

8 Use the Report Wizard to create a report based on the No Equipment Required query. The report should display the *ExerciseName*, *MuscleGroup*, and *Type* fields, in that order. Do not specify any grouping levels. Sort the report by the *ExerciseName* field in ascending order.

9 Save the report, naming it *No Equipment Required*.

10 Use the Print Preview feature to preview the report.

11 Print the No Equipment Required report or submit the completed database as directed by your instructor.

12 Close the No Equipment Required report and then the database.

Completed Review 2, Clients Query

Completed Review 2, No Equipment Required Report

Completed
Review Preview

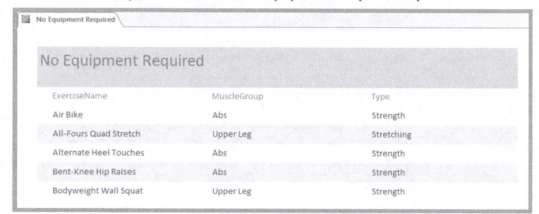

Review 3   Finding and Reporting Information from a Community Volunteers Database

Skills   Create a query in Design view, use more than one table in a query, and create and preview a report

Scenario   You have set up a database to track the number of hours students spend performing community service. You first find out how many hours students are volunteering at the various organizations and then present this information in a report.

Steps

Student
Data Files

1 Open the student data file named **C3R3-CommunityService**. If a security warning appears immediately below the ribbon, click the Enable Content button. If a second security warning appears, click the Yes button.

2 Query the database to find out how many volunteer hours are being spent at each organization. In Design view, add the Organizations table and then the Volunteer Hours table to create your query. The query should display the *OrganizationName* field (from the Organizations table), *StudentID* field, and *Hours* field, in that order. Sort the query by *OrganizationName* in ascending order.

3 Run the query to confirm that it is selecting the correct records.

4 Save the query, typing Volunteer Hours by Organization as the query name, and then close the query.

5 Use the Report button to create a report based on the Volunteer Hours by Organization query.

6 Display the Group & Sort pane and then group the report by the *OrganizationName* field.

7 Sort the report by the *Hours* field.

8 Close the Group & Sort pane.

9 AutoFit the *Record Count* cell.

10 Save the report, naming it *Volunteer Hours by Organization*.

11 View the report in Print Preview view.

12 Change the print orientation to landscape.

13 Print the Volunteer Hours by Organization report or submit the completed document as directed by your instructor.

14 Close the Volunteer Hours by Organization report and then the database.

Completed Review 3, Volunteer Hours by Organization Query

OrganizationName	StudentID	Hours
City Soup Kitchen	ND07	1.50
City Soup Kitchen	SS06	2.00
City Soup Kitchen	ES08	2.50
City Soup Kitchen	RS08	1.50
City Soup Kitchen	LP06	2.25
Literacy for the Little	TI08	2.25
Literacy for the Little	MJ07	2.00
Literacy for the Little	LP06	3.50
Literacy for the Little	VS07	3.00
Sandy Beaches	SK06	3.00
Sandy Beaches	VS07	3.00
Sandy Beaches	ES08	2.25

Completed
Review Preview

Completed Review 3, Volunteer Hours by Organization Report

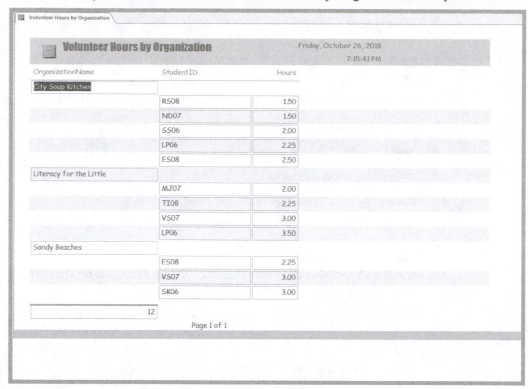

Completed
Review Preview

SNAP Exercises

 SNAP *If you are a SNAP user, go to your SNAP Assignments page
to complete additional exercises available for you.*

Unit 5 **Access**

Skills Assessment

Assessment 1 **A Movie Database**

Skills **CH1:** Open and navigate a database, enter data, edit data, format a datasheet **CH2:** Create a table, create a form, enter data in a form **CH3:** Create a query in Design view, create and preview a report

Scenario You manage a business that streams movies online. You have created a database to store data on the available movies. You now need to create a table to store information about each movie and then create a form and use it to enter records in the database. Finally, you will run a query to find all the PG-13 movies in your database, and create a report based on that query.

Steps

Student Data Files

1 Open the student data file named **U5A1-Movies**.

2 Create a new table in Design view.

3 Define the table to have the following fields and data types:

Field Name	Data Type
ID	Number
Title	Short Text
Rating	Lookup Wizard

4 In the Lookup Wizard dialog box, specify your own values in a single column, typing the following entries:

PG
PG-13
R

Close the dialog box when you are done.

5 Make the *ID* field the primary key.

6 Save the table, typing Movies as the table name, and then close the table.

7 Use the Form button to create a form based on the Movies table.

8 Switch to Design view and then narrow the width of the fields in the form by dragging the *ID* field to the 5-inch mark on the ruler.

9 Save the form, naming it *Movies*.

10 Switch to Form View.

11 Use the Movies form to enter the following records in the database:

ID	Title	Rating
3155	The Man from U.N.C.L.E	PG-13
3479	Minions	PG
3480	Jurassic World	PG-13
3529	Ant-Man	PG-13
4690	Fantastic Four	PG-13
5134	Inside Out	PG

12 Change the *ID* number of the first record to 3185.

13 In Design view, create a query to find all movies rated PG-13. Display the fields *Title* and then *Rating* in your query.

14 Run the query and AutoFit the *Title* column.

15 Save the query, typing PG-13 Movies as the query name.

16 Print the PG-13 Movies query or submit the query result as directed by your instructor. Close the query.

17 Use the Report button to create a report based on the PG-13 Movies query.

18 Sort the report in ascending order by the *Title* field.

19 AutoFit the *Record Count* cell.

20 Save the report, naming it *PG-13 Movies,* and then close the report.

21 Run the PG-13 Movies report. Print the report or submit the report result as directed by your instructor. Close the report.

22 Close the database and submit the completed file as directed by your instructor.

Completed Assessment 1, PG-13 Movies Query

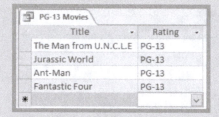

Completed Assessment 1, PG-13 Movies Report

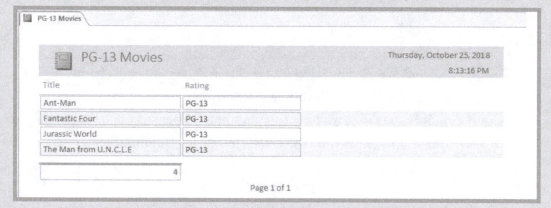

Completed
Assessment
Preview

Assessment 2 A Computer Support Service Database

Skills   **CH1:** Open and navigate a database, enter data **CH2:** Create a table, create a form, enter data in a form **CH3:** Create a query in Design view, use the Report Wizard

Scenario You run a computer support website. Users pay either a six-month fee of $60 or an annual fee of $120 to access online computer help. You need to create a database to store information about your subscribers. After creating a table and entering customer records, you then run a query to find the customers who have paid $60 for six months of service, and create a report based on that query.

Steps

Student
Data Files

1 Open the student data file named **U5A2-ComputerSupport**.

2 Create a new table in Design view.

3 Define the table to have the following fields and data types:

Field Name	Data Type
ID	Number
LastName	Short Text
FirstName	Short Text
JoinMonth	Lookup Wizard
Fee	Currency

4 In the Lookup Wizard dialog box, specify your own values in a single column, typing the following entries:

January
February
March
April
May
June
July
August
September
October
November
December

5 Make the *ID* field the primary key.

6 Save the table, typing Customers as the table name. Close the table.

7 Use the Form button to create a form based on the Customers table.

8 Switch to Design view and then narrow the width of the fields in the form by dragging the right border of the *ID* field to the 5-inch mark on the ruler.

9 Save the form, naming it *Customers*.

10 Switch to Form View.

11 Use the Customers form in Form view to enter the following records in the database:

ID	LastName	FirstName	JoinMonth	Fee
5155	Mitchell	Paul	September	120.00
5167	Ableson	Michelle	October	60.00
5169	Quinn	Terry	October	60.00
5170	Samuels	Jennifer	November	60.00
5180	Watson	Robert	November	120.00
5290	Simpson	Ann	December	120.00
5400	Gregory	Michaela	December	60.00

12 Close the Customers form.

13 Use the Query Design button to create a query of all customers who have paid a fee of $60. Display the *LastName*, *FirstName*, and *Fee* fields, in that order, in the query.

14 Run the query.

15 Save the query, typing $60 Customers as the query name.

16 Print the $60 Customers query or submit the query result as directed by your instructor. Close the query.

17 Use the Report Wizard button to create a report based on the $60 Customers query. Include the *LastName*, *FirstName*, and *Fee* fields in the report. Do not add any grouping levels.

18 Sort the report in ascending order based on the *LastName* field and accept the default report layout.

19 Save the report, naming it *$60 Customers*, and then close the report.

20 Run the $60 Customers report. Print the report or submit the report result as directed by your instructor. Close the report.

21 Close the database and submit the completed file as directed by your instructor.

Completed Assessment 2, $60 Customers Query

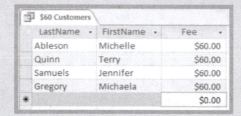

Completed Assessment 2, $60 Customers Report

Completed
Assessment
Preview

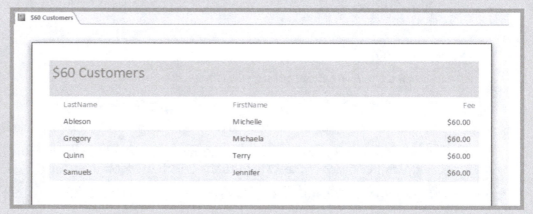

Assessment 3 **A Rental Car Database**

Skills   **CH1:** Open and navigate a database, enter data, sort data, filter data **CH2:** Create a table, enter data in a table, create a form, enter data in a form **CH3:** Create a query in Design view, create and preview a report

Scenario You run a car rental company and are setting up a database to track your car inventory. You will start by creating a table and adding records to the table. You then create a form for adding additional records to the table. You will then filter data, run a query to find all the 2017 cars in your inventory, and create a report based on that query.

Student Data Files

Steps

1 Open the student data file named **U5A3-RentalCars**.

2 Create a new table in Design view.

3 Define the table to have the following fields and data types:

Field Name	Data Type
CarYear	Number
Make	Short Text
Model	Short Text
Color	Short Text
Mileage	Number

4 Save the table, typing Cars as the table name. Do not add a primary key to the table.

5 Enter the following records in the Cars table:

CarYear	Make	Model	Color	Mileage
2016	Ford	Fiesta	Red	37295
2016	Ford	Fiesta	Blue	12000
2015	Honda	Civic	Brown	10000

6 Sort the records by car year in ascending order.

7 Save and close the table.

8 Use the Form button to create a form based on the Cars table.

9 Use the Logo button to insert the student data file **U5A3-Car** in the form header.

10 AutoFit the logo.

11 Save the form, naming it *Cars*.

12 Use the Cars form in Form view to enter the following records in the database:

CarYear	Make	Model	Color	Mileage
2015	Honda	Civic	Black	12000
2017	Chevrolet	Cruze	Black	8550
2017	Chevrolet	Cruze	White	22000

13 Print the Cars form or submit the completed form as directed by your instructor. Close the form.

14 Open the Cars table and filter the data to display 2016 cars.

15 Print the Cars table or submit the filtered table as directed by your instructor.

16 Remove the filter, save the table, and then close the table.

17 Use the Query Design button to create a detail query of all 2017 cars. Display the *CarYear*, *Make*, *Model*, and *Mileage* fields, in that order, in the query.

18 Run the query.

19 Save the query, typing 2017 Cars as the query name.

20 Print the 2017 Cars query or submit the query result as directed by your instructor. Close the query.

21 Use the Report button to create a report based on the Cars table.

22 Group the report by the *Make* field.

23 Use the Report Layout Tools Page Setup tab to change the page orientation to landscape.

24 AutoFit the *Record Count* cell.

25 Save the report, typing Car Inventory as the report name.

26 Print the Car Inventory report or submit the completed report as directed by your instructor. Close the report.

27 Close the database and submit the completed file as directed by your instructor.

Completed Assessment 3, Cars Form

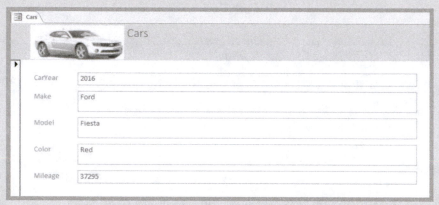

Completed Assessment 3, Filtered 2016 Cars Table

Completed Assessment 3, 2017 Cars Query

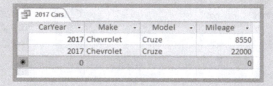

Completed Assessment 3, Car Inventory Report

Completed
Assessment
Preview

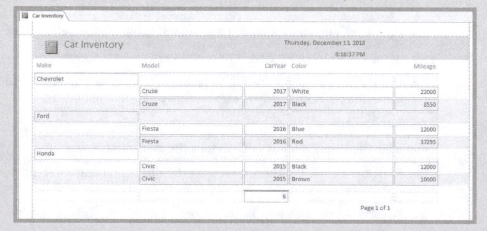

PowerPoint Chapter 1 **Creating a Presentation**

Study Resources

Study Resources

A chapter-based presentation with audio support, Margin Tips & Hints, and other study resources are available from this ebook page.

Features Review

Features Review

The Features Review available from this ebook page presents 10 multiple-choice questions to help you reinforce your understanding of the features covered in this chapter.

If you are a SNAP user, go to your Assignments page to complete the Features Review.

Skills Review

Review 1 **Traveling Safely with a Dog**

Skills   Open PowerPoint and insert a slide, enter text on slides, add notes, apply a layout and run a slide show, and organize slides using the Slide Sorter feature

Scenario   You have been asked to update a presentation used to advise pet owners about safe practices when traveling with a pet. Edit the file provided to improve the presentation.

Steps

Student Data Files

1 Open the student data file named **C1R1-Travel** and save the file as **C1R1-Travel-Lastname**, but replace *Lastname* with your last name.

2 Type your name and the current date in the subtitle placeholder on the first slide so the information appears on two separate lines.

3 Apply the Picture with Caption layout to Slide 4, *Relax and Have Fun*.

4 Add the following speaker note to Slide 4, *Relax and Have Fun*.
   If you plan carefully, a trip with a pet can be fun and rewarding.

5 At the end of the presentation, insert a new slide with the Title and Content layout.
   a. Type Accommodations as the slide title.
   b. Type the following content as three bullet points:
      Review pet policies, such as not allowing dogs to be left alone in the room.
      Use white noise to help muffle sounds in the hallway and keep your dog quiet.
      Help your dog soothe himself by providing a bedtime chew stick or favorite toy.

6 Review the slide order and reorganize the slides so they appear in the following sequence:
      Slide 1: *Travel Safely with Your Dog*
      Slide 2: *Accommodations*
      Slide 3: *Medical*
      Slide 4: *Vehicle*
      Slide 5: *Relax and Have Fun*

7 Save the file.

8 Run the presentation. *Hint: Click the Slide Show tab and then click the From the Beginning button.*

9 Submit the completed presentation to your instructor.

Completed Review 1

Travel Safely with Your Dog
Student Name
Current Date

Accommodations
- Check in advance to be sure the place you are staying allows dogs.
- Review pet policies, such as not allowing dogs to be left alone in the room.
- Use white noise to help muffle sounds in the hallway and keep your dog quiet.
- Help your dog soothe himself by providing a bedtime chew stick or favorite toy.

Medical
- Check that vaccinations and parasite treatments are up-to-date.
- Learn the location of a vet near your travel location in advance.
- Have medical records available.
- Keep a first aid kit available.
- Bring food, treats, and lots of water.
- Be sure your dog has a microchip, in addition to a collar and tags, to help you locate her if she wanders.
- Bring pictures of your dog.

Vehicle
- Take your dog for short rides before starting on a longer journey.
- Allow your dog to travel on an empty stomach to avoid car sickness.
- Make water available throughout the trip.
- Do not permit your dog to travel in the open bed of a truck or with his head out an open window.
- Restrain your pet in an approved crate, seatbelt, harness, or booster seat.
- Provide ample opportunity for your dog to relieve himself and get exercise.
- Never leave your dog unattended in a closed vehicle.

Relax and Have Fun
Izzie (yellow vest) and Keiko enjoying a boat ride with Ken

Completed Review Preview

Review 2 Creating Effective Presentations

Skills   Enter text on slides, apply a layout and run a slide show, and apply a theme

Scenario You are working on a presentation that will be delivered to your company's sales reps at the national sales meeting. This presentation will remind the reps how to make interesting and engaging presentations.

Steps

Student
Data Files

1 Open the student data file named **C1R2-EffectivePresentations** and save the file as **C1R2-EffectivePresentations-Lastname**, but replace *Lastname* with your last name.

2 Type your name and the current date in the subtitle placeholder on the first slide so the information appears on separate lines.

3 In Slide 2, demote (increase the list level of) the four bullet points that follow the *Order the slides* bullet point and the one bullet point that follows *Storyboard*. **Hint:** *Highlight the text from* Title slide *to* Ending *and then click the Increase List Level button in the Paragraph group on the Home tab.*

4 Apply the Basis theme to the presentation.

5 Apply the third variant to the presentation.

6 Save the presentation.

7 Run the presentation.

8 Submit the completed presentation to your instructor.

Completed Review 2

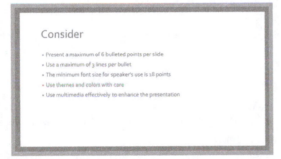

Completed
Review Preview

Review 3 Telling Others about Therapy Cats

Skills   Enter text on slides, add notes, apply a layout and run a slide show, apply a theme, and organize slides using the Slide Sorter feature

Scenario   Therapy animals visit people who are sick or disabled to help them feel better. A colleague has drafted a presentation about two certified therapy cats for you to use in telling others about the program. Update and customize the presentation by making it more eye-catching and adding speaker notes.

Steps

Student
Data Files

1   Open the student data file named **C1R3-CatsWork** and save the file as **C1R3-CatsWork-Lastname**, but replace *Lastname* with your last name.

2   Place the slides into the correct sequence:
    Slide 1: *Cats at Work*
    Slide 2: *Topics*
    Slide 3: *Growing Up*
    Slide 4: *Pet Therapy*
    Slide 5: *Certified Therapy Animals*
    Slide 6: *Certifying Gerald and Marcel*
    Slide 7: *Story of a Visit*
    Slide 8: *Retirement*

3   Type your name and the current date in the subtitle placeholder on the first slide so the information appears on two separate lines.

4   Update Slide 5, *Certified Therapy Animals*, as follows.
    a. Apply the Comparison layout.
    b. In the left column, type Dogs as the column heading. In the content box below, type the following bullets:
    Tested every 2 years
    On personality and demeanor
    On obedience
    c. In the right column, type Cats as the column heading. In the content box below the heading, type the following bullets:
    Tested every 2 years
    On personality and demeanor
    Not on obedience because cats rarely respond to obedience commands

5   Add the following speaker notes to Slide 5, *Certified Therapy Animals*:
    Not every animal will earn certification. The animal must be patient and have the necessary skills.

6   Add a sentence to the end of the speaker notes for Slide 6, *Certifying Gerald and Marcel*:
    They were patient and loving.

7   Apply the Ion theme to the presentation. Do not apply a variant.

8   Save the file.

9   Run the presentation.

10   Submit the completed presentation to your instructor.

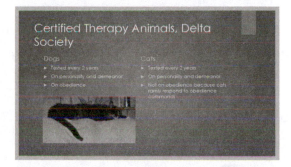

Completed
Review Preview

SNAP Exercises

 **SNAP**

*If you are a SNAP user, go to your SNAP Assignments page
to complete additional exercises available for you.*

PowerPoint Chapter 2 **Customizing a Slide Show**

Study Resources

Study
Resources

A chapter-based presentation with audio support, Margin Tips & Hints, and other study resources are available from this ebook page.

Features Review

Features
Review

The Features Review available from this ebook page presents 10 multiple-choice questions to help you reinforce your understanding of the features covered in this chapter.

If you are a SNAP user, go to your Assignments page to complete the Features Review.

Skills Review

Review 1 **Formatting a Presentation on US Presidents**

Skills Change formatting in Slide Master view, change the color scheme in Slide Master View, and add a footer

Scenario Each student in your history class will deliver a presentation on four presidents of the United States. You have been assigned the first four presidents. Update the presentation by adding a theme, modifying colors and fonts, and adding a footer.

Steps

Student
Data Files

1 Open the student data file named **C2R1-Presidents** and save the file as **C2R1-Presidents-Lastname**, but replace *Lastname* with your last name.

2 In Slide 1, insert a new line after the dates *1789-1817* in the subtitle placeholder and then type your name, a comma, and the current date on the new line.

3 Insert a new Slide 2 with the Title and Content layout, typing Topics as the slide title and these four bulleted points as the slide content:
George Washington
John Adams
Thomas Jefferson
James Madison

4 Apply the Retrospect theme to all slides. Do not select a variant.

5 Modify the slide master as follows:
   a. Apply the Bauhaus 93 font style to the text in the title placeholder on all slides. *Hint: Click the top thumbnail in the slide thumbnails pane (you may need to scroll up) and then click in the title placeholder text in the slide pane before making changes.*
   b. Apply the Slipstream theme color to all slides.

6 Close Slide Master view and return to Normal view.

7 Add to all presentation slides a three-part footer that contains the current date, the text Source: https://www.whitehouse.gov/1600/Presidents, downloaded 8/5/2015, and the slide number. Do not show the footer on the title slide.

8 Save the presentation.

9 Preview the presentation.

10 Submit the completed presentation to your instructor.

Completed Review 1

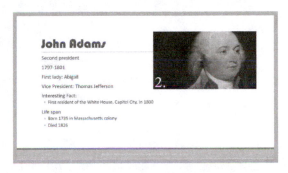

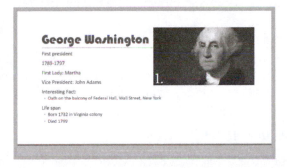

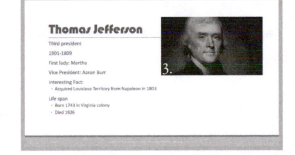

Completed
Review Preview

Review 2 Enhancing Your Presentation on US Presidents

Note: This assignment can be done immediately if you are comfortable inserting and sizing images using the Online Pictures button in the Pictures group on the Insert tab as directed in Unit 3 (Word), Chapter 3, Skills 8–10. As an alternative, return to this assignment after completing Unit 6 (PowerPoint), Chapter 3, Skills 1 and 2.

Skills   Insert a graphic in Slide Master view and hide a slide master element on a slide

Scenario Enhance the presentation on US presidents that you formatted in Review 1 by inserting a graphic in the slide master and then making adjustments so the graphic will appear on most, but not all, slides.

Steps

Student
Data Files

1 Open the file named **C2R1-Presidents-Lastname**, the file you saved in Skills Review 1, and save the file as **C2R2-Presidents-Lastname**.

2 In Slide Master view, select the Title and Content layout slide master used by Slides 2–6 (third slide from the top in the slide thumbnails pane). You will use this slide master to add an image to all slides that use the Title and Content layout.
   a. Use the Online Pictures button in the Images group on the Insert tab and the search term US flag 13 to locate an image of the original Betsy Ross flag with 13 stars in a circle and 13 stripes (or an image similar to the image shown in the Completed Review 2 images below). Insert the image.
   b. Change the width of the image to 1.67".
   c. Position the image so the lower right corner of the image fits exactly in the lower right corner of the content placeholder. *Hint: The image is in the correct location when the right and bottom lines that surround the image are sitting on the right and bottom lines of the placeholder.*

3 Close Slide Master view and return to Normal view.

4 Select Slide 2 (*Topics*) and then use the Format Background pane on the Design tab to hide the flag image on that slide.

5 Save the presentation.

6 Preview the presentation and verify that the flag image displays on Slides 3–6.

7 Submit the completed presentation to your instructor.

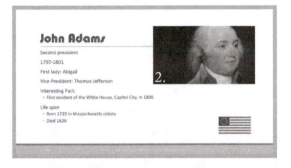

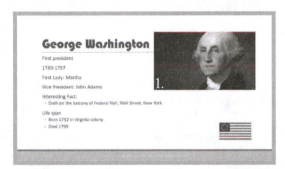

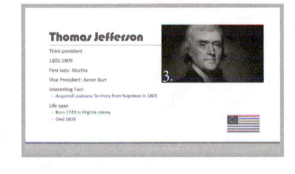

Completed
Review Preview

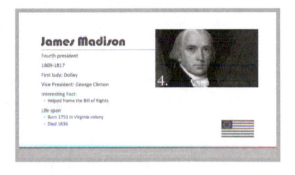

Review 3 Improving an Animal Shelter Presentation

Skills   Change formatting in Slide Master view and add a footer

Scenario   You are preparing a presentation about pet adoption. Improve the presentation by adding a theme and a footer.

Steps

Student
Data Files

1 Open the student data file named **C2R3-Shelter**, and save the file as **C2R3-Shelter-Lastname**, but replace *Lastname* with your last name.

2 Apply the Banded theme to all slides. Do not select a variant.

3 On all slides, including the Title layout slide (Slide1), insert a footer that includes your name, the current date, and the slide number.

4 Modify the slide master as follows:
   a. Change the size of all the footer text to 18 points. ***Hint:*** *In Slide Master view, click the top (and largest) thumbnail in the slide thumbnails pane (you may need to scroll up). In the slide pane, click the left footer placeholder (which displays the date), select the text, and then change the font size to 18 points. Repeat this procedure for the middle and right footer placeholders.*
   b. Center the text in the middle footer placeholder (which displays your name).
   c. On the Two Content Layout (used by slides 2, 6, and 8) change the font color for the Title placeholder to Green in the Standard Colors section of the Font Color drop-down gallery.

5 Close Slide Master view and return to Normal view.

6 Save the presentation.

7 Preview the presentation and verify that the title is green on Slides 2, 6, and 8.

8 Submit the completed presentation to your instructor.

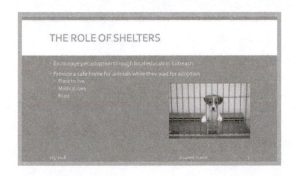

Completed
Review Preview

SNAP Exercises

 SNAP

*If you are a SNAP user, go to your SNAP Assignments page
to complete additional exercises available for you.*

PowerPoint Chapter 3
Adding Media Elements and Effects

Study Resources

Study Resources

A chapter-based presentation with audio support, Margin Tips & Hints, and other study resources are available from this ebook page.

Features Review

Features Review

The Features Review available from this ebook page presents 10 multiple-choice questions to help you reinforce your understanding of the features covered in this chapter.

If you are a SNAP user, go to your Assignments page to complete the Features Review.

Skills Review

Review 1   Adding Media to a Presentation on Car Racing

Skills   Insert a picture, format a picture, add transitions, and add sound

Scenario Add interest to a presentation of historical points about car racing by inserting, sizing, and positioning an image; adding transitions; and adding a sound.

Steps

Student Data Files

1 Open the student data file named **C3R1-CarRacing** and save the file as **C3R1-CarRacing-Lastname**, but replace *Lastname* with your last name.

2 In Slide 1, type your name and the current date on two separate lines in the subtitle placeholder.

3 In the slide master, make the following modifications:
   a. Insert the student data file named **C3R1-RaceCar1** (a picture file) on all slides, regardless of the slide layout. *Hint: Use the Office Theme Slide Master layout (the top thumbnail in the slide thumbnail pane).*
   b. Size the picture to a height of 1.1 inches and a width of 1.65 inches. Then move the picture to the horizontal position 10.77 inches from the top left corner and to the vertical position 5.66 from the top left corner. *Hint: Use the Size options and Position options in the Size & Properties section of the Format Picture pane.*
   c. Close Slide Master view.

4 Add to all the presentation slides a footer that displays the slide number. Do not show the footer on the title slide.

5 In Slide 6, use the Format Background pane on the Design tab to hide the **C3R1-RaceCar1** picture and then insert the student data file named **C3R1-RaceCar2** (a picture file) in the content placeholder on the right side of the slide.

6 Add the following transitions:
   a. Slide 2: *Crush* (in the *Exciting* section)
   b. Slides 3–5: *Page Curl* (in the *Exciting* section)
   c. Slide 6: *Pan* (in the *Dynamic Content* section)
   d. Slide 7: *Flip* (in the *Exciting* section)

7 In Slide 6, use the Transitions tab to add the Drum Roll sound. Set the duration to 1.30.

8 Save the presentation.

9 Preview the presentation.

10 Submit the completed presentation to your instructor.

Completed Review 1

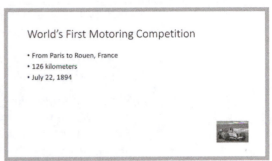

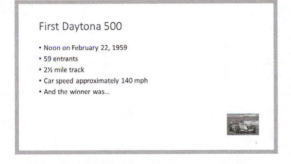

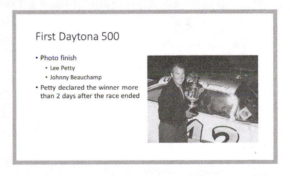

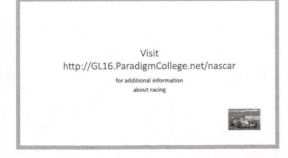

Completed
Review Preview

Review 2 Adding Media to a Presentation about Donny

Skills   Format a picture and insert a video

Scenario Enhance a presentation about the adoption of a newborn kitten by adding a theme, modifying the background, repositioning a picture, and adding a video.

Steps

Student
Data Files

1 Open the student data file named **C3R2-Donny**, and save it as **C3R2-Donny-Lastname**, but replace *Lastname* with your last name.

2 In Slide 1, type your name and the current date on two separate lines in the subtitle placeholder.

3 On all slides except Slide 1 (the title slide), insert a footer containing the slide number and the text Donny: A Great Find.

4 Apply the Savon theme to all slides. The first color variant is selected by default. Do not change the color variant.

5 In Slide 1 (the title slide), use the Format Background pane on the Design tab to hide the background graphic.

6 In Slide 1 (the title slide), move the picture of Donny so it does not cover a portion of the title text. Move the image to the horizontal position 9.24 inches from the top left corner and to the vertical position 0.54 inches from the top left corner. *Hint: Use the* Position *options in the* Size & Properties *section of the Format Picture pane.*

7 In Slide 8, change the layout to Comparison and then make the following additional changes:
   a. In the heading text box on the left, type Donny likes….
   b. In the heading text box on the right, type See Donny doing some tricks!.
   c. In the content box on the right, insert the student data file named **C3R2-Donny8Tricks**, which is a video file. *Hint: Use the* Video on My PC *option in the Video drop-down list in the Media group on the Insert tab.*

8 Save the presentation.

9 Preview the presentation. Test the video to be sure it plays.

10 Submit the completed presentation to your instructor.

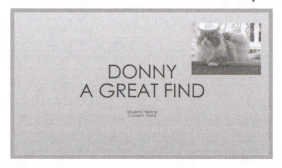

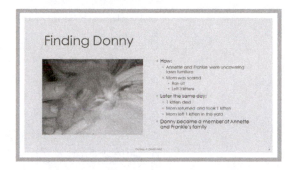

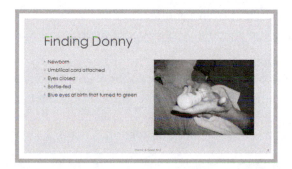

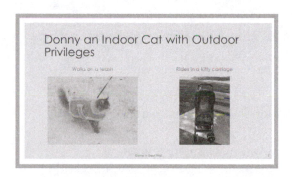

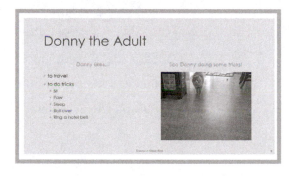

Completed
Review Preview

Review 3 Adding More Media to Your Presentation about Donny

Skills   Insert a picture, add transitions, add animations, and choose animation effects

Scenario   Enhance the newborn kitten presentation from Review 2 by adding an additional image and appropriate animations and transitions.

Steps

Student Data Files

1   Open **C3R2-Donny-Lastname**, the file you saved in Skills Review 2, and save it as **C3R3-Donny-Lastname**, but replace *Lastname* with your last name.

2   In Slide 3, make these changes:
   a. Change the layout to Two Content.
   b. Insert an online picture of a house, typing the search term children in yard to locate the picture shown in Completed Review 3 (or an image similar to that one).

3   Use the Animations tab to add the following entrance and emphasis animations to the image in each slide. Use the Animation Pane to set each animation to start after the previous animation is done. **Hint:** *Click the image to select it and then add the animation.*
   a. Slide 3: *Teeter* animation
   b. Slide 4: *Zoom* animation and *Object Center* effect option
   c. Slide 5: *Wheel* animation and *8 Spokes* effect option
   d. Slide 9: *Grow & Turn* animation

4   In Slide 6, add the following animations:
   a. Image on left: *Fly In* animation and *From Left* effect option
   b. Image on right: *Fly In* animation and *From Right* effect option

5   In Slide 7, add the following animations.
   a. Image on left: *Shape* animation, *In* direction effect option, and *Box* shape effect option
   b. Image on right: *Shape* animation, *In* direction effect option, and *Diamond* shape effect option
   c. Set each animation to start after the previous animation is done.

6   Add the following transitions:
   a. Slide 1: *Split* transition and *Vertical Out* effect option
   b. Slides 2–8: *Push* transition and *From Right* effect option
   c. Slide 9: *Reveal* transition and *Through Black From Right* effect option.

7   Save the presentation.

8   Preview the presentation.

9   Submit the completed presentation to your instructor.

Completed Review 3, Slide 3

Completed Review Preview

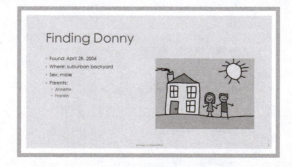

SNAP Exercises

 *If you are a SNAP user, go to your SNAP Assignments page to complete additional exercises available for you.*

PowerPoint Chapter 4
Completing, Running, and Sharing Your Show

Study Resources

Study Resources

A chapter-based presentation with audio support, Margin Tips & Hints, and other study resources are available from this ebook page.

Features Review

Features Review

The Features Review available from this ebook page presents 10 multiple-choice questions to help you reinforce your understanding of the features covered in this chapter.

If you are a SNAP user, go to your Assignments page to complete the Features Review.

Skills Review

Review 1   Completing a Presentation about Keeping a Cat Healthy

Skills   Check spelling and run a show for an audience

Scenario   You are completing a presentation about Pete, an adopted cat with medical issues, to deliver on Adoption Day at your local Humane Society. As the final steps in your preparation, review the content for spelling errors and add a footer.

Steps

Student Data Files

1   Open the student data file named **C4R1-Healthy,** and save the file as **C4R1-Healthy-Lastname**, but replace *Lastname* with your last name.

2   In Slide 1 (the title slide), type your name and the current date on two separate lines in the subtitle placeholder. If necessary, move an image so your entire name and the date are visible.

3   On all slides except the title slide, insert a footer displaying the slide number and the text *Keeping Pete Healthy*.

4   Check the spelling of the slide content and correct any errors you find. Check your corrections against the Completed Review 1 slides shown below.

5   Save the file.

6   Preview the presentation.

7   Submit the completed presentation to your instructor.

8   If possible, deliver the presentation to an audience.

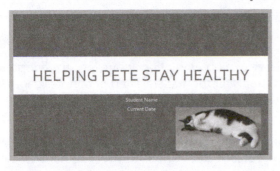

TOPICS

- About Pete
- Medical Problems
- Medications
- Just Your Average Cat!

ABOUT PETE

- Domestic longhair cat
- Male
- 13 years old
- Adopted at age 3
- Lives with
  - Phoenix, a 10-year-old male cat
  - Human parents – Alicia and Aharon

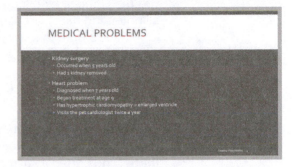

MEDICAL PROBLEMS

- Kidney surgery
  - Occurred when 5 years old
  - Had 1 kidney removed
- Heart problem
  - Diagnosed when 7 years old
  - Began treatment at age 9
  - Has hypertrophic cardiomyopathy – enlarged ventricle
  - Visits the pet cardiologist twice a year

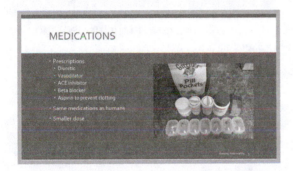

MEDICATIONS

- Prescriptions
  - Diuretic
  - Vasodilator
  - ACE inhibitor
  - Beta blocker
  - Aspirin to prevent clotting
- Same medications as humans
- Smaller dose

GIVING THE MEDICATIONS TO PETE

- Pills are quartered or halved
  - Cut a week's supply
  - Place in a day-of-the-week holder to avoid confusion
- Pills are placed in soft treats
  - Placed into a hole in center of treat
  - Make sure Pete eats the entire treat, including the pill

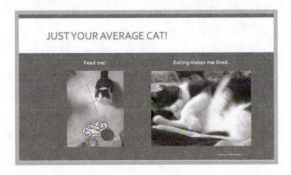

JUST YOUR AVERAGE CAT!

Feed me!

Eating makes me tired.

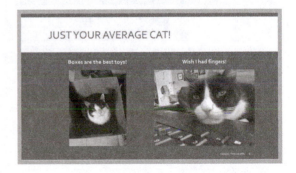

JUST YOUR AVERAGE CAT!

Boxes are the best toys!

Wish I had fingers!

JUST YOUR AVERAGE CAT!

Pete (right) hanging out with his pal, Phoenix (left)

Completed
Review Preview

Review 2 Printing Handouts and Notes for a Presentation about Keeping a Cat Healthy

Skills Print speaker notes with a header

Scenario You are preparing to deliver your presentation about Pete, the adopted cat with medical issues. Print handouts for the audience and print notes pages that you can use as a guide while presenting.

Steps

1 Open **C4R1-Healthy-Lastname**, the file you saved in Skills Review 1, and save it as **C4R2-Healthy-Lastname**, but replace *Lastname* with your last name.

2 Use the <u>Edit header & footer</u> link in the Print backstage area to add a header and a footer to all notes and handouts pages as follows:
   a. Include a date that will update automatically.
   b. Include a page number.
   c. Include a header, typing your name in the *Header* box.

3 Save the file.

4 Print one set of handouts for your audience, including all the slides in the presentation, three slides per page. ***Hint:*** *In the Print backstage area, click the* Full Page Slides *arrow in the* Settings *category of the Print panel, and then click the* 3 Slides *option in the* Handouts *section of the drop-down list.*

5 Print one set of notes pages, including all the slides in the presentation, to use as talking points during delivery of the presentation.

6 Submit both sets of printouts to your instructor.

Completed Review 2, Handouts

Completed
Review Preview

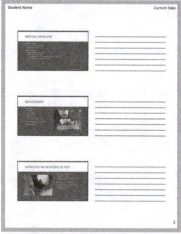
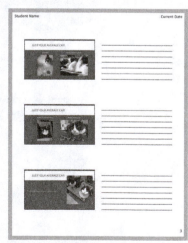

Completed Review 2, Notes Pages

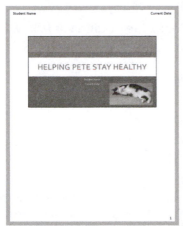

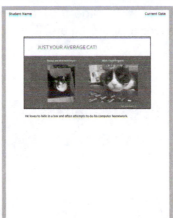

Completed
Review Preview

Review 3 Setting Up a Presentation about Keeping a Cat Healthy

Skills Run a show for an audience, rehearse timings, set up a show, and present online

Scenario Your presentation about Pete, the adopted cat with medical issues, was popular. A local veterinarian's office has asked for a copy of the presentation to share with human parents of ill animals. You decide to set timings so the slide show progresses without a speaker present.

Steps

1 Open **C4R2-Healthy-Lastname**, the file you saved in the previous exercise, and save the file as **C4R3-Healthy-Lastname**, but replace *Lastname* with your last name.

2 Add the *Random* transition to all slides in the presentation.

3 Complete one of the following options:

   a. **Option 1:** Set the timings for the slides in the presentation as follows:

      Slide 1: 0:00:04

      Slide 2: 0:00:04

      Slide 3: 0:00:06

      Slide 4: 0:00:08

      Slide 5: 0:00:07

      Slide 6: 0:00:09

      Slide 7: 0:00:05

      Slide 8: 0:00:05

      Slide 9: 0:00:05

   b. **Option 2:** Add customized timings to all slides in the presentation using the Rehearse Timings button on the Slide Show tab. ***Hint:*** *It is difficult to determine how long each slide should appear. To achieve realistic timings, read every line on the slide slowly, as if you are seeing it for the first time; spend a moment looking at each of the images on the slide; and then move to the next slide.*

   c. **Optional extension activity:** Record a narration of the slide's notes and set the timing to match the length of the narration. ***Hint:*** *Review the Taking It Further: Recording a Slide Show feature in Skill 3 of this chapter. Find a quiet place to record the narration. Ask for a microphone if necessary. Speak slowly and give the viewer enough time to look at the images on each slide before moving to the next slide.*

4 Set up the slide show to play automatically when browsed at a kiosk.

5 Save the file.

6 Preview the presentation.

7 Submit the completed presentation to your instructor.

8 If possible, present the slide show online using the Office Presentation Service. Ask your instructor where to send the email link.

Completed Review 3, Slide Sorter View

Completed
Review Preview

SNAP Exercises

Unit 6 **PowerPoint**

Skills Assessment

Assessment 1 Helping Middle School Students Learn about Pets

Skills   **CH1:** Enter text on slides, add notes, apply a theme **CH2:** Change formatting in Slide Master view, add a footer **CH3:** Insert and position a picture, format a picture, add transitions, add animations, choose animation effects, format individual slides **CH4:** Check spelling, run a show for an audience, print speaker notes with a header

Scenario   You work for a veterinarian who has been asked to present a workshop about pets at the local middle school. You decide to create a slide presentation to share engaging pictures and basic information about some healthy patients. You enhance the presentation to keep the middle school students interested. You also print handouts to distribute to teachers so they can discuss the animals later with their students, and speaker notes for you to read during the presentation.

Steps

Student
Data Files

1   Open the student data file named **U6A1-PetsPlay**, and save the file as **U6A1-PetsPlay-Lastname**, but replace *Lastname* with your last name.

2   In Slide 1, type your name and the current date on two separate lines in the subtitle placeholder.

3   Apply the Berlin theme to all slides. Do not apply a variant.

4   Adjust the theme color as specified below. *Hint: Select the indicated slides, click the More button in the Variants group, click the Colors option in the drop-down list, right-click the color name in the second drop-down list, and then click the Apply to Selected Slides command in the pop-up list.*
    a. Slides 3–6: *Green Yellow*
    b. Slides 7–10: *Blue Warm*
    c. Slides 11–14: *Blue II*

5   Open Slide Master view. In all slides that use the Picture with Caption layout (Slides 6, 10, 14, and 18), change the font size for the text in the left content box to 24 points. Close Slide Master view.

6   Add transitions and effects as follows:
    a. Slides 1–2: *Split* transition and *Vertical Out* effect option
    b. Slide 3: *Prestige* transition
    c. Slides 4–6: *Push* transition and *From Right* effect option
    d. Slide 7: *Ripple* transition and *Center* effect option
    e. Slides 8–10: *Push* transition and *From Right* effect option
    f. Slide 11: *Glitter* transition and *Hexagons from Left* effect option
    g. Slide 12–14: *Push* transition and *From Right* effect option
    h. Slide 15: *Wind* transition and *Right* effect option
    i. Slides 16–18: *Push* transition and *From Right* effect option

7   Add a picture to each of the four section header slides as described below, using the student data files provided. Change the size of each image to 4 inches high. Do not adjust the width. Place each image in the left center of the slide at the horizontal position 0.75 inches from the top left corner and the vertical position 1.6 inches from the top left corner.

    a. Slide 3: **U6A1-Izzie**

    b. Slide 7: **U6A1-Riley**

    c. Slide 11: **U6A1-Hannah**

    d. Slide 15: **U6A1-Mollie**

8. Add the following entrance and emphasis animations. Set each animation to start after the previous animation is done.

    a. Slide 3 image: *Float In* animation and *Float Up* effect option

    b. Slide 7 image: *Zoom* animation and *Slide Center* effect option

    c. Slide 11 image: *Grow & Turn* animation

    d. Slide 15 image: *Grow/Shrink* animation and *Larger* effect option

9. On all slides except the title slide, insert a footer that displays an automatically updating date, the text Cats and Dogs at Play, and the slide number.

10. Add a header and a footer to the Notes and Handouts pages. Type your name and an automatically updating date in the header. Type Cats and Dogs at Play and the page number in the footer.

11. Type the following speaker notes in the notes pane:

    a. **Slide 2:** Meet some amazing pets. Izzie, Riley, and Mollie are funny and interesting dogs. Hannah is a remarkable cat.

    b. **Slide 16:** Lhasa Apso dogs were raised by Tibetan monks as guard dogs. They have a fierce bark even though they are small.

12. Check the presentation for spelling errors and correct any errors you find.

13. Print one set of handouts for your audience, including all the slides in the presentation, six slides horizontal per page. **Hint:** *Open the Print backstage area, click the* Full Page Slides *arrow in the Settings section of the Print panel, and then click the* 6 Slides Horizontal *option in the* Handouts *section of the drop-down list.*

14. Print one copy each of the notes page for Slides 2 and 16. **Hint:** *Click the* Print All Slides *arrow in the Settings category, click the* Custom Range *option in the drop-down list, and then type* 2, 16 *in the* Slides *box.*

15. Save the file.

16. Preview the presentation.

17. Submit the completed file, the handouts, and the notes pages to your instructor.

Completed
Assessment
Preview

Completed Assessment 1, Handouts

Completed
Assessment
Preview

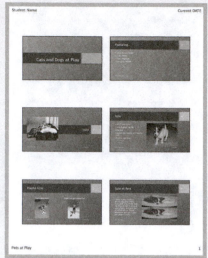

Completed Assessment 1, Notes

Completed
Assessment
Preview

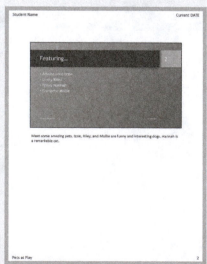

Assessment 2 Creating Arithmetic Flashcards

Skills   **CH1:** Enter text on slides, apply a layout and run a slide show, apply a theme, organize slides using the Slide Sorter feature **CH2:** Change formatting in Slide Master view, change the color scheme in Slide Master view **CH3:** Insert and position a picture, format a picture, add transitions, add animations, choose animation effects, format individual slides **CH4:** Run a show for an audience, present online

Scenario   Your neighbor's son is learning arithmetic and needs some help. Create an arithmetic flash card tutorial using PowerPoint. Make it interesting and fun as well as educational so that he practices often.

Steps

Student
Data Files

1   Open the student data file named **U6A2-FlashCards**, and save it as **U6A2-FlashCards-Lastname**, but replace *Lastname* with your last name.

2   Use the Slide Sorter to place the slides in the following order:
   a. Slide 1: *Flash Cards*
   b. Slide 2: *Addition*
   c. Slide 3: *Subtraction*
   d. Slide 4: *Multiplication*
   e. Slide 5: *Division*
   f. Slide 6: *Exponentiation*
   g. Slide 7: *Interpreting Your Score*

3   Switch to Normal view. In Slide 1, type your name and the current date on two separate lines in the subtitle placeholder.

4   Open Slide Master view. You will use the Slide Master for steps 5 through 8.

5   In the slide thumbnails pane, click the Comparison layout thumbnail. In the slide pane, modify the left and right content placeholders (displaying bulleted text) as described below. ***Hint:*** *You can select and modify each placeholder separately, or modify both placeholders at the same time. To modify the placeholders separately, click the left placeholder, complete Steps 5a through 5d, click the right placeholder, and then complete Steps 5a through 5d again. To modify both content placeholders at the same time, select both placeholders using the Click, Shift-Click method—click one, hold down the Shift key while you click the other, and then release the Shift key—and then complete Steps 5a through 5d.*
   a. Turn off bullets. ***Hint:*** *Click the Bullets button in the Paragraph group on the Home tab.*
   b. Center the text.
   c. Middle align the text. ***Hint:*** *Click the Align Text button in the Paragraph group on the Home tab and then click the* Middle *option in the drop-down list.*
   d. Change the font size to 40 points.

6   Continuing to use the Comparison layout, center the text of the left and right caption placeholders (above the content placeholders).

7   Modify the left caption and content placeholders as described below, using commands in the Drawing group on the Drawing Tools Format tab:
   a. Apply the theme color Black, Text 1 to the shape outline.
   b. Apply the theme color Blue, Accent 5, Lighter 40% to the shape fill.

8   Modify the right caption and content placeholders as described below, using commands in the Drawing group on the Drawing Tools Format tab:
   a. Apply the theme color Black, Text 1 to the shape outline.
   b. Apply the theme color Green, Accent 6, Darker 25% to the shape fill.

9 Return to Normal view.

10 In Slides 1 and 7 (the title and final slides), apply the Retrospect theme and select the second variant (green). **Hint:** *Select the indicated slides in the slide thumbnail pane before applying the theme.*

11 In Slide 7 (the final slide), insert a shape as follows:
   a. Use the Shapes arrow in the Illustrations group on the Insert tab to insert the Smiley Face shape.
   b. Use commands in the Format Picture pane to change the size of the shape to 3.5 inches high and 3.5 inches wide.
   c. Use commands in the Format Picture pane to place the shape at the horizontal position 8.0 inches from the top left corner and the vertical position 2.25 inches from the top left corner.
   d. Use commands in the Shape Styles group on the Drawing Tools Format tab to apply the standard color Yellow to the shape fill and the theme color Dark Green, Text 2 to the shape outline.

12 Add transitions as follows:
   a. Slide 1: *Fade* transition, *Smoothly* effect option
   b. Slides 2–6: *Cover* transition, *From Bottom-Right* effect option
   c. Slide 7: *Shape* transition, *Circle* effect option

13 Add animations as follows:
   a. Open Slide Master view.
   b. In the slide thumbnail pane, click the Comparison layout thumbnail. **Hint:** *This is the same layout that you modified in Steps 5–8 of this assessment.*
   c. Select the right caption and content placeholders using the Click, Shift-Click method.
   d. Apply the *Appear* animation and the *As One Object* effect option.
   e. Return to Normal view.

14 Save the file.

15 Run the presentation to preview your work.

16 Submit the completed file to your instructor.

17 **Optional extension activity:** Run the show manually for an audience or present the slide show online using the Office Presentation Service. If you present online, ask your instructor where to send the email link.

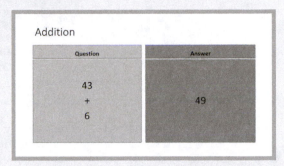

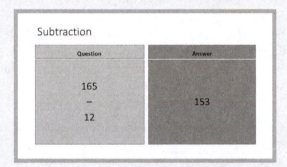

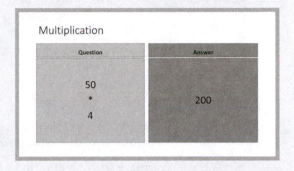

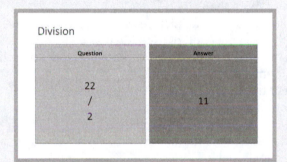

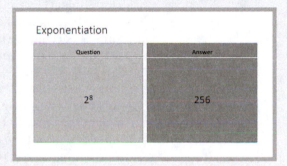

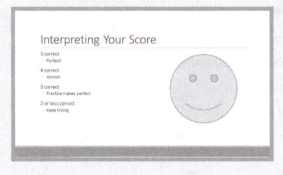

Completed
Assessment
Preview

Assessment 3 Personifying an Inanimate Object

Skills   **CH1:** Open PowerPoint and insert a slide, enter text on slides, add notes, apply a layout and run a slide show, apply a theme **CH2:** Change formatting in Slide Master view, add a footer **CH3:** Insert and position a picture, format a picture, add transitions, add sound, add animations, choose animation effects **CH4:** Check spelling, run a show for an audience, rehearse timings, set up a show, print speaker notes with a header, present online

Scenario   Create an engaging presentation that personifies an object—that is, gives the object human qualities. You will title the presentation *My Life as <a(n) Object>*, replacing *<a(n) Object>* with the name of the inanimate object that will be the focus of the presentation. For example, a presentation titled *My Life as a Pencil* will personify a pencil. The pencil might complain about shrinking when it is sharpened, describe its happiness the first time a child picks it up and writes her name, or celebrate the success of helping a student earn a perfect score on a math test. The presentation should demonstrate creativity and be fun to deliver. Share the presentation as specified by your instructor.

Steps

1   Create a new PowerPoint file, and save it as **U6A3-Object-Lastname**, but replace *Lastname* with your last name.

2   Create the presentation according to the following specifications:
   - Include at least five, but not more than eight, slides.
   - At least three slides should contain online pictures or your own photos. Include the source of each image in the Notes section of the slide it appears on.
   - Use the Title Slide layout on Slide 1 and use two additional layouts on other slides.
   - Use one or more design themes.
   - Apply at least two different transitions to two or more slides.
   - Apply one appropriate sound to play during a transition.
   - Animate the images and/or text on two or more slides.
   - In all slides except the title slide, add a footer that includes an automatically updating date, your name, and the slide number.
   - On the master slide, make a modification to the title font that will affect all slides.
   - Include speaker notes that can be used if you are asked to deliver the presentation.
   - Set timings that are appropriate for individuals viewing the slide show without a speaker.
   - **Optional extension activity:** Add both narration and timings.

3   Ensure your slides are set to automatically advance using the timings you have added.

4   Check your spelling in the slides and the notes.

5   Ask your instructor whether you will be sharing the presentation online or delivering it in class. If you are to deliver the presentation in class, make the required adjustments so the slides advance manually.

6   Save the file.

7   Preview the presentation.

8   Submit the completed file to your instructor.

Unit 7 Integrating Office Applications

Study Resources

Study Resources

A chapter-based PowerPoint presentation with audio support, Margin Tips & Hints, and other study resources are available from this ebook page.

Skills Assessment

Assessment   An Electronic Menu and Ordering System for a Restaurant

Skills: Skills used will vary depending on choices you make. Requirements include use of Word, Excel, Access, and PowerPoint, and integration of Access with Excel.

Scenario: You manage a neighborhood restaurant, and lately several customers have complained that the service is very slow. The restaurant staff are often busy, and customers have to wait long periods of time to get a menu and place an order. You meet with the owner of the restaurant to express your concern about this issue, and he asks you to help him explore options for setting up an electronic menu and ordering system. You agree to do the following:

- **Part A:** Create a PowerPoint presentation that explains the benefits of using an electronic menu and ordering system.
- **Parts B:** Create a letter identifying at least three vendors who specialize in electronic menu and ordering technology.
- **Part C:** Create a database that contains a table of menu items by name, description, and price, and that also contains an order query.
- **Part D:** Create an Excel worksheet that generates a bill for an order and that compares the costs of the items in the bill.
- **Part E:** Submit the four project files to your instructor.

Steps, Part A

Go online and research the benefits of using an electronic menu and ordering system. Create a PowerPoint presentation that you can deliver, in person, to explain the benefits to the restaurant owner. *Hint: You may want to copy the data into Microsoft OneNote and include your research notes so they are easily available for use in your presentation.*

1   Start with a new, blank presentation or a PowerPoint template.

2   Include six to eight slides total.

3   Use the Title Slide layout for the first slide.

4   For the slides following the title slide:
   a. Use at least two different slide layouts.
   b. In at least four slides, insert one or more images; each image should include a caption that indicates its source.
   c. Include text on every slide in addition to the slide title.
   d. Include at least two different transitions within the presentation.
   e. In three slides, animate one or more objects. Each animation should start on a mouse click because you will deliver the presentation in person.

    f. On the final slide, list all the sources you used while researching and creating your presentation.

    g. On every slide except the title slide, insert a footer that includes a date that updates automatically, your name, and the slide number.

5 Apply a theme to the presentation.

6 Include speaker notes that you will use to deliver the presentation to the restaurant owner.

7 Save the presentation with the name **U7A1-A-Emenu-Lastname**, but replace *Lastname* with your last name.

Steps, Part B

After you deliver your presentation on the benefits of an electronic menu and ordering system, the restaurant owner decides to implement an electronic system and asks you to identify possible vendors in your area. You go back online to research vendors. ***Hint:*** *Try search terms such as* electronic menu system vendors, electronic restaurant menu vendors, *and* online ordering system vendors. Then create a letter to the restaurant owner, providing the vendor information.

1 Based on your online research, select at least three vendors. At a minimum, for each choice, record the vendor name, the product name (that is, the name of the electronic menu and ordering system), and the URL where you found the information. ***Hint:*** *You may want to copy the data into Microsoft OneNote so it is easily available for use in your letter.*

2 Start with a new, blank Word document or a Word letter template.

3 Create a well-worded letter that provides the vendor information.
    a. Start with a heading that includes the current date, the name of the recipient (the restaurant owner), and the name and address of the restaurant. ***Hint:*** *You can use information from a local restaurant or make up information.*
    b. List at least three vendors. At a minimum, for each choice, include the vendor name, the product name (that is, the name of the electronic menu and ordering system), and the URL where you found the information.
    c. Include your name in the closing of the letter.

4 Save the letter as **U7A1-B-Emenu-Lastname**, but replace *Lastname* with your last name.

Steps, Part C

Given all the information you have supplied, the restaurant owner decides to implement an electronic menu and ordering system. You are asked to create an Access database that contains the names, descriptions, and prices for items that will be included in the electronic menu, and to create a database query that will display an order.

1 Create a new, blank database and name it **U7A1-C-Emenu-Lastname**, but replace *Lastname* with your last name. ***Hint:*** *To create a new, blank desktop database, open Access and then click the* Blank desktop database *template in the opening screen.*

2 Create one table in the database and name the table Menu.

3 The table will need the following fields. Select the appropriate data type for each field.
    ItemName
    ItemDescription
    ItemCost
    OrderedItem (This field will contain *Yes* if the item is being ordered and will be empty otherwise.)

4 Enter the data for at least 20 menu items. Do not enter any data in the *OrderedItem* field. ***Hint:*** *You can use data from the menu of a local or online restaurant, or make up data.*

5   Create one query in the database and name the query Order.

6   Set the query to select the item name and cost for each item marked Yes in the *OrderedItem* field.

7   Test the query by selecting three items you might like to order and entering *Yes* in the *OrderedItem* field for each of those items. Run the query to be sure only the three items marked Yes are listed.

Steps, Part D

Eventually, the restaurant owner will add a feature that allows customers to pay using a debit or credit card and prints a simple itemized receipt. However, that feature will not be available when you pilot the new system. For the pilot, you will create an Excel workbook that displays a bill for an order on one sheet tab and a chart comparing the costs of the items ordered on a second sheet tab. The chart worksheet will be made available to customers who want to split the cost of a bill based on the item price.

1   Open the Access database you created in Part C of this project, named **U7A1-C-Emenu-Lastname**, and run the Order query with three items ordered (with *Yes* entered in three items in the *OrderedItem* field).

2   Open a new, blank Excel workbook and copy the rows from the Access Order query result into a blank worksheet beginning at row 3.

3   In row 1 of the worksheet, type the name of the restaurant.

4   In row 2, type the column heading Item for column 1 and type the column heading Cost for column 2.

5   Below the order information you inserted in Step 2, compute the order total using a function.

6   Below the total, compute three tip options as follows:
    a. Display the tip amount at 15%, 18%, and 20% of the total.
    b. Also show the total bill amount with tip for each of the three options.

7   Format the worksheet using appropriate number formats.

8   Size the columns and rows and add color, borders, and other visual formatting to make the worksheet easier to read.

9   On a separate sheet in the same workbook, create a pie chart that compares the various costs of the items ordered. Enhance the pie chart as follows:
    a. Add a chart title.
    b. Remove the chart legend.
    c. Label the slices with the cost and the percent.

10 Name the worksheet containing the data *Customer Bill* and the worksheet containing the pie chart *Order Comparison*.

11 Add a footer to both worksheets. In the footer, type your name and today's date.

12 Save the Excel workbook as **U7A1-D-Emenu-Lastname**.

Steps, Part E

Submit the four project files to your instructor:

U7A1-A-Emenu-Lastname

U7A1-B-Emenu-Lastname

U7A1-C-Emenu-Lastname

U7A1-D-Emenu-Lastname